GRASSHOPPERS &
LOCUSTS

THE PLAGUE OF THE SAHEL

THE PANOS INSTITUTE

LONDON   PARIS   WASHINGTON

Published by Panos Publications Ltd
9 White Lion Street
London N1 9PD, UK

British Library Cataloguing in Publication Data
A catalogue record for this book is available from the British Library

Funding for *Grasshoppers and Locusts* was provided by the US Agency for International Development, Bureau for Africa, through the Africa Emergency Locust/Grasshopper Assistance (AELGA) Project (698-0517). Panos also received funding from Miseoreor, Germany, for some initial research.

Any judgement expressed in this document should not be taken to represent the view of any funding agency. Signed articles do not necessarily reflect the views of Panos or any of its funding agencies.

John Rowley, who has worked for the British government on pest control in the Sahel and is now agricultural adviser to Oxfam, researched and wrote this dossier with Olivia Bennett. Other writers are acknowledged where their contribution appears in the text.

The Panos Institute is an information and policy studies institute, dedicated to working in partnership with others towards greater public understanding of sustainable development. Panos has offices in London, Paris and Washington DC.
For more information about Panos contact Juliet Heller, Panos London.

Managing editor: Olivia Bennett
Production: Sally O'Leary
Illustrations: Philip Davies
Cover design: The Graphic Partnership
Printed in Great Britain by The Bath Press, Bath

Contents

Acknowledgements

This dossier is dedicated to the memory of Soumana Sounterra, the Director of the National Plant Protection Service in Mali (Service National de la Protection des Végétaux) from 1987 to his tragic death in 1990. He was a man of great skill and dedication and the inspiration for the good work achieved by the SNPV since its creation. Mali contains some of the most important breeding sites of the Desert Locust and other species. It also suffers from attacks by a large range of grasshoppers. The SNPV therefore plays a key role in the control of the major regional insect pests. Soumana led the SNPV so well that, despite massive handicaps, it managed to carry out successful anti-locust campaigns and gain considerable international prestige.

During the years (1985-88) that I worked with Soumana his desire to be allowed to run an efficient and effective service for the benefit of Malian farmers was continually beset with difficulties. This dossier describes some of the problems that Soumana and his counterparts in neighbouring countries have faced. Some of these stem from the nature of the Sahelian environment and of the insects which inhabit it; some are due to the current state of knowledge and skill in combating these insects. But some problems are due to the conflicting priorities or uncoordinated activities of the many different players involved in the fight against locusts and grasshoppers—politicians, donors, scientists, manufacturers, agency workers and technicians.

This dossier is intended to help in the understanding and resolution of the problems—the genuine and the unnecessary —which characterise locust and grasshopper control, and to stimulate a serious discussion of the issues and the need for a longer-term approach.

Many people and organisations have helped in its preparation, including members of the Food and Agriculture Organization in Rome, the Natural Resources Institute of

Britain and PRIFAS in Montpellier, France. Thanks are also due to Heywote Bekele, Simon Burne, James Deane and Wendy Davies, but we would like to acknowledge in particular the valuable contributions made by Walter Knausenberger (Bureau for Africa, USAID) and George Popov.

John Rowley

CHAPTER 1

Breaking the cycle

Over the past 20 years, millions of dollars have been spent fighting locusts in the Sahel, a vast swathe of Africa stretching from Mauritania in the west to the Horn in the east (see map on p13). Much of this money was made available in the form of periodic emergency aid, leaving little behind it in terms of acquired local skills and infrastructure, or an increased research base on which to build for the next campaign. The flow of funds all too often echoed the irregular progress of the plagues: huge sums would pour into the Sahel and then dwindle away to a thin trickle, insufficient to support long-term reform and development of pest control programmes.

The frustration of those who argue that the costs of control should be approached more as a sort of insurance premium, with the emphasis on regularity and reliability of funding, was highlighted in 1988, when the largest Desert Locust plague since the 1950s swept across the Sahel. After some 25 years during which, apart from some minor upsurges, the threat of plagues seemed almost to have disappeared, it was a sobering reminder of the damage these insects can inflict. At its height the plague covered an area from Cape Verde in the Atlantic to Pakistan and India, and some 43 countries were affected—nearly one-fifth of the Earth's surface.

An Age-Old Threat

Locust plagues are as old as farming itself. The Bible records that when the Israelites were enslaved in Egypt in 1491 BC, Moses called on God to visit Pharaoh's land with a devastating plague: "They covered the surface of the land till it was black with them. They devoured all the vegetation and all the fruit of the trees that the hail had spared. There was no green left on tree or plant throughout all Egypt [1]."

In 800 BC the prophet Joel wrote: "After the cutter-locusts finish eating your crops, the swarmer-locusts will take what's left! After them will come the hopper-locusts! And the stripper locusts, too [2]!" Pliny attributed famines in Cyrenaica (800,000 deaths) and Tunisia (300,000 deaths) to locust plagues. Sixteenth-century Portuguese traveller Francisco Alvares, recalling time spent in Ethiopia and the devastation wrought by locusts, wrote:

> Their multitude, which covers the earth and fills the air, is not to be believed, they darken the light of the sun....[whenever] they come the earth is left as though it had been set on fire....We found the roads full of men, women and children, on foot and some in their arms, with their little bundles on their heads...it was a pitiful thing to see them [3].

More recent accounts tell similar stories of regular massive plagues throughout this century. Most descriptions take as their reference point the major definitive historical survey by Zena Waloff [4]. The renowned ecologist Charles Krebs records: "Since 1908 there have been four major plagues [of the Desert Locust], ranging in duration from seven to 13 years and alternating with short periods of population recession lasting up to six years [5]." The last period of major activity which was relatively continuous, albeit with peaks and troughs, was

The extent of major plagues of the Desert Locust: 1908-1971

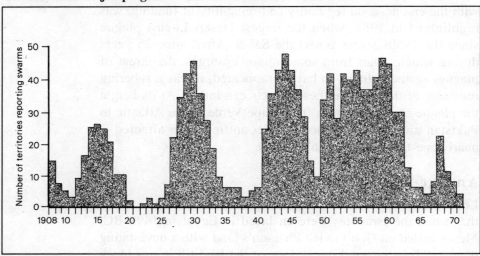

In this chart, as in other attempts to demonstrate the extent of plagues, the estimates are not of the numbers of locusts or of swarms, but only of the numbers of places where swarms were reported. This highlights the immense difficulty of obtaining quantitative data on locusts. The Sahel is so vast, so sparsely populated and so difficult to survey thoroughly that there is no option but to rely on imprecise indicators of pest numbers. Despite this vagueness, the numbers of places reporting swarms still gives a fairly accurate picture of the history, severity and extent of plagues in past years.

Source: Hemming, C F, *The Locust Menace*, Centre for Overseas Pest Research, London, 1974

during 1939-1963.

   Most of these quotes refer to the activities of the Desert
Locust and it is this species which is really the source of
plagues and the target of donor activities today. In the Sahelian
region in particular this locust is the problem, since the
Migratory Locust appears to have gone into permanent
recession, and the Tree Locust is a relatively recent and less
damaging pest (see pp28-29). Red and Brown Locusts
primarily affect Southern Africa, although the former can
move up into Sudan during plagues, but it is the Desert
Locust—not least because of its special habit of breeding in
remote areas which means populations can grow undetected to
dangerous numbers—which presents the greatest threat.

   While much of this dossier concentrates therefore on
activities to control Desert Locusts, it also deals with the other
equally important if less dramatic pests in the Sahel:
grasshoppers. Indeed, many hold the view that grasshoppers,
especially those species which tend to multiply rapidly and
move in swarms, present a more serious threat to crop
production than intermittent locust attack. The damage
grasshoppers cause at any one time may not be on the scale of
a plague, but it happens every year and the recurrent losses
cause severe hardship to rural communities.

*A Malian
entomologist
holds a Desert
Locust caught
in a millet field.*

*Climate
is the
overriding
factor*

The 1986-88 plague

Since the early 1960s, except for a few short-lived outbreaks, the Sahel had been remarkably free of locust problems. While there has been some debate about the exact size and frequency of locust plagues (see bar chart, p2) and the different causes of their arrival and disappearance, there is general agreement that climate is the overriding factor. The periods of drought since the mid-1960s, coupled with regular surveys of seasonal breeding grounds and preventive control operations, helped to keep locust numbers down. And it was the good rains of 1985 which seem to have stimulated the increased breeding which triggered the 1986-88 plague.

The scale of this plague took many people by surprise after such a long period of apparent quiescence, although it followed a pattern which with hindsight can be described as predictable. Yet opportunities to act in the early part of the plague build-up were missed, national services were unprepared and staff were poorly trained, data was imprecise, donor policies were uncoordinated and diverse, and equipment and pesticides arrived late. The end result was millions of dollars spent on emergency control measures, which contributed little towards long-term improvements in the security of Sahelian farming.

Why was this plague not more successfully controlled? During the early 1980s, the Sahel was in the grip of continuing drought. One effect was a general lessening of insect activity and while there were significant exceptions—for example, the millet head miner—most pests posed less of a problem than in years of higher rainfall. In 1985 the rains were relatively good and the population of the Senegalese Grasshopper (*Oedaleus senegalensis*) reached dangerous levels. In 1986 and 1987, 4.6 million hectares in 10 Sahelian and West African countries received aerial or ground insecticide treatments against grasshoppers.

In spite of this, the prevailing attitude was that conditions had not changed enough to create problems with the principal locust species. Yet it was widely known that the two regional organisations responsible for locust control in East and West Africa—Organisation Commune de Lutte Anti-Acridienne et de Lutte Anti-Aviaire (OCLALAV) and the Desert Locust Control Organisation for Eastern Africa (DLCO-EA) (see p76)—had not been carrying out routine survey or control operations for some years, since member states had been *The cost* failing to pay their contributions [6]. *of aerial*

In 1985 breeding populations of the Desert Locust were *spraying was* observed in parts of the Arabian peninsula. Control operations *astronomical* were apparently ineffective. During 1986 there was further breeding in Ethiopia and Sudan. Towards the end of 1986 reports began to come in of more successful breeding in Niger, Mali and Mauritania. The abundant rains of 1987 provided further good breeding conditions, especially in Ethiopia, Sudan, Niger, Mali and Mauritania, and also in Chad, where the conflict with Libya prevented effective survey and control operations. Some breeding also occurred in the prohibited disputed areas north of Mauritania. Indeed, the insects made the most of all the areas of political tension where, ironically, the breeding conditions were particularly favourable. The total area treated for Desert Locusts in Sahelian countries from 1985-89 was some 5,550,000 hectares.

At the end of 1987, swarms of locusts left the remote "outbreak" areas where they had bred and moved to new "invasion" areas. Huge numbers of locusts were borne by the wind as far as Algeria and Tunisia, attacking orchards on the Mediterranean coast. Many reached Morocco where large-scale control operations started in October 1987.

By early 1988, the threat to Sahelian cropland was clearly extremely serious and a vast campaign to destroy the swarms was well underway. Large amounts of money were mobilised, although in many respects the campaign also benefited from the fact that there had been extensive control operations against grasshoppers during the previous two years, and some supplies and equipment were already in place.

Dozens of mostly donor-provided aircraft flew thousands of hours in pesticide spraying operations. The cost of this alone was astronomical, especially when measured against the national budgets of the countries affected. Yet, given the potential for destruction, one of the most surprising aspects of this plague was that so little damage was done in the Sahel. Luck played a considerable part, as many swarms descended on fields which had already been harvested or where they could do little damage to crops. Other swarms moved on quickly, before they destroyed everything.

The way the plague collapsed was equally remarkable. Towards the end of 1988 large numbers of swarms, apparently

Seasonal movements and breeding areas of the Desert Locust

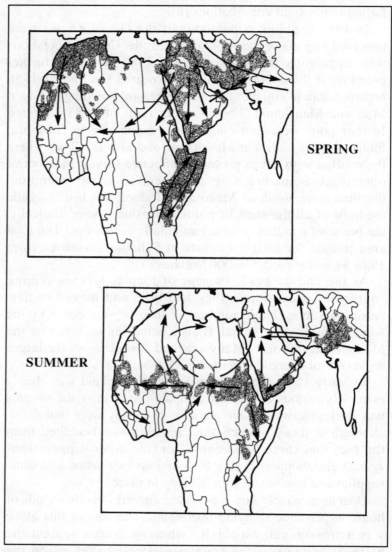

SPRING

SUMMER

heading for Morocco, were carried by unusual wind patterns out over the Atlantic Ocean. Most died, and those that reached the Caribbean—a remarkable feat with no recorded precedent—failed to breed. Those that made it to Morocco met with unfavourable cold, dry conditions and were largely destroyed by the country's plant protection services, backed up by outside help. Most observers had expected the plague to continue for several years, but early in 1989 it was clear that the main threat had passed.

Organisations were slow in raising the alarm

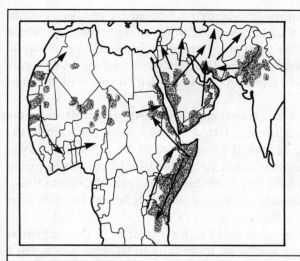

WINTER

Locusts need moist soil for egg-laying and the growing hoppers and developing adults need fresh vegetation on which to feed, so the insects are only able to breed during rainy periods. If the rains are extensive, especially following prolonged drought, several generations of locusts can breed in a given area, producing swarms which are able to fly considerable distances to find further suitable breeding conditions.

Breeding areas are thus dictated by seasonal rains, and the movement of swarms between these areas by the prevailing winds. The spring rains fall mainly in North Africa, the Middle East, southern Iran and Pakistan. The resulting swarms then move south and west as these areas dry out, and this is when the Sahelian croplands are most at risk. Breeding then takes place during the summer rains in Mauritania, Mali, Niger, Chad, Sudan, Ethiopia and southern Arabia. Swarms also move southeast to the monsoon rainfall areas of Pakistan and India.

After summer breeding, most swarms tend to move north and northwest. There is a winter breeding season around the Red Sea coasts, which is where historically the majority of plagues have originated. In East Africa, breeding occurs between October and December (the short rains) and from February to June (the long rains).

Source: Adapted from *Locust Handbook*, Natural Resources Institute, Chatham, UK, 1988

Mishaps and misjudgments

Information from the field on the increasing Desert Locust activity in 1985 and 1986 was slow in reaching DLCO-EA, the Food and Agriculture Organization (FAO) and OCLALAV. They in turn were slow in raising the due alarm. Some information did get through by the recognised routes to the countries concerned and the international community, but apparently it was not received with any sense of urgency. The situation was seriously compounded by the fact that crop protection staff in Sahelian countries were already fully occupied with problems of grasshoppers, principally the Senegalese Grasshopper.

***There was
a lack of
good data***   The constraints on surveying caused by conflict clearly contributed to the paucity of information, but there was a lack of good data even from areas where survey work was possible. Most absent were authoritative predictions of the likely scale of "upsurge", the build-up of swarms which can mark the start of a plague.

The situation was complicated by a loss of confidence in the regional organisations. OCLALAV was moribund. While the experience and technical competence of its remaining survey and control teams was not in doubt, lack of resources meant their mobility and effectiveness were severely constrained. Thus, even if it had called for a full-scale locust campaign, its credibility was already in question.

The reasons underlying the failure of the regional organisations are dealt with more fully in Chapter Seven, but a number of factors contributed to their inactivity, including a lack of perceived danger from locusts, competing pressures on national budgets, and the difficulties over cohesive action which are endemic to regional structures.

If 1985 had seen a return to thorough survey work, there might have been time to collect sufficiently accurate data to alert crop protection organisations and donors of the need to mount control operations. By 1987 it was too late for preventive measures. It was clear that considerable breeding had taken place and that locusts would be invading vulnerable areas in 1988.

The Need For New Approaches

This brief summary of the course of the 1986-88 plague illustrates the complex nature of efficient control operations against the Desert Locust. Accurate up-to-date information is essential and can only be achieved by detailed survey work. Good communication is necessary across enormous distances, often to inaccessible areas. Fast action and flexibility are crucial. None of these criteria was fulfilled. Once the upsurge had started, extra resources were supplied but too late to have sufficient impact, especially since some were inappropriate. For example, pesticides and equipment new to the region were donated, yet there was no time for the necessary staff training. In the end, unfavourable climatic conditions had the greatest impact on the collapse of the plague.

This dossier, which includes comments from Sahelian

farmers and plant protection agents, examines the many controversies in the battle being waged in the Sahel against locusts and grasshoppers—a battle in which donors have largely been the driving force. This dossier argues that in spite of the millions of dollars spent, especially on emergency campaigns, the livelihood of the Sahelian farmer is no less vulnerable than in the past to the threat of locust plague or grasshopper damage.

This Malian farmer's crops have been devastated by grasshoppers. They cause serious damage every year, whereas locusts only threaten crops at times of plague.

There is, however, a growing receptivity to new ideas and directions, an increasing national capacity to address the problem and, perhaps most important of all, the old assumptions on which control campaigns have been run are beginning to be questioned. In a special report on the 1986-88 plague by the US Office of Technology Assessment it was stated that "response to the African locust and grasshopper outbreaks has commonly been based on faulty assumptions...[7]." Too many gaps and weaknesses in knowledge allow for confusion over the best methods to adopt. The extent to which locust plagues cause famine, the extent to which the use of pesticides effectively prevents plagues, the extent to which widespread spraying is damaging the enviroment, and the extent to which chronic grasshopper damage is more of a threat to Sahelian agriculture than locust

Plagues arouse much media coverage and donor activity, but as the threat dies down, so does the interest. There remains a need for a more sustained approach to locust and grasshopper control.

Sahel faces new locust threat

More aid money for anti-locust battle in Afri-
Organisations invol-
control the sw-
pests
the

Locusts Threatening North Africa

insecticide at present to stop it
are no new concentration-
lot of them in Alger-
way."
"One exper-
cent of
no

the cities of Casablanca, Rabat, Fez
Marrakech. "We are in a state of
eral alert, said Edouard Saouma, direc-
general of the United Nations Food
Agriculture Organization. "Swift and
cisive action is needed to avoid a major
gional food crisis.
There   also high concentrations of the
locust·   desert of Algeria. Experts say
th   ead back this way, threat-
more as well as others.
ve also been spotted
cent weeks.
ome neighboring
ved the best of
ion, though
believe is
ve mo-
over
to

Plague of Africa

AFRICA is bracing itself for
a locust invasion, the largest
in 30 years, at a time when
the continent's locust contro
organisations are collaps-
clim. The Migratory Locust
beco-   trol Organization fo
Every   powers after the
of 1930 to mon
weather delta, it tra
ground for
African m
en their m
non has b
Of, how
will enc
for years

The locusts are coming

To combat the spreading threat
locusts to African countries.
locust should now shift to
tative measures, according
ukas Brader of the FAO
en participating in a
ing of the Inter-s
Drought C
LSS)

Mali fights menace of 'Le Cricquet'

The shooting down of an American crop-spraying
plane by rebel missile fire in the Western Sahara
highlights the continuing battle against locusts.
Mary Anne Fitzgerald reports from Bamako, Mali

..meets twice daily, while
.center room is staffed roun
. meteorologists, army and air
nel, communications opera
civilians.
"The situation changes d

Ghiles, recently in North Africa, on the worst plague of locusts in 30 years

war against the scourge of the Maghreb

plague of reb anew.   rains have seldom been

drought
Shortages of pesticide, airc
vehicles and spraying equipr
have hampered operations to
trol the locusts, but aid f
Western European countries

attack—these are just some of the areas which need to be re-evaluated because there is not enough hard evidence to justify "business as usual".

Donors and national plant protection services are increasingly aware that fresh ideas must be considered and new approaches tried. Another plague on the scale of the 1986-88 one could as easily build up—and luck may not be on the Sahel's side this time. If technical and institutional capacities are not strengthened and if more sustainable strategies are not developed, the farmers of the Sahel will continue to be vulnerable to devastating crop losses.

CHAPTER 2

Farming the Sahel

Sahel is Arabic for the "shore" or "edge" of the Sahara desert. Much of the region, which sweeps from Mauritania in the west across 7,000 kilometres to the Horn of Africa, has low rainfall and poor soils. Yet millions of Sahelians manage to make a living from the semi-arid land, growing crops and herding animals. Over the last 25 years or so, however, prolonged drought and increased human activity has led to a deterioration of the already fragile environment.

Desertification is accelerating, productivity is declining, pastures are disappearing and more and more people are being forced to give up the struggle to survive in one of the toughest farming environments in the world. The pressure has been relentless, since there have been too few consecutive good years to allow the environment to regenerate and farmers' reserves or herds to build up. In addition, along with some positive political changes and moves towards greater democratisation, the Sahel has seen accelerating conflict—at local, national and regional levels. Political changes have sometimes generated greater tensions and violence. Another key factor in the rising conflict has been environmental degradation and so the increased competition for resources [1]. But whatever the origin, conflict usually causes further environmental damage and adds to the complex cycle of deterioration.

The Environment

It is hard to say what type of soil we prefer because the most important factor determining the land's productivity is the rain. Those of us who have the opportunity to cultivate different areas do so. Some farm on the bottom of a valley where the land is wetter and they also cultivate an area with hard soils, and then another with sandy soils. In this way, they don't lose everything—whatever way the rainfall fluctuates [2].
Group of women, Burkina Faso

Rainfall determines the environment of the Sahel. It occurs

Jeremy Harley/Panos Pictures

Planting millet in Burkina Faso. In the adverse conditions of the Sahel, farming strategies aim at risk reduction rather than risk avoidance.

mostly between July and September, although rain earlier and later than this can have important effects locally. Rain is associated with the movement of the Inter-tropical Convergence Zone (ITCZ). This is a band of very unsettled weather that moves north during the beginning of the rainy season and then retreats south, signalling the end of the rains. Over the last two decades in particular, the annual rains have tended to move less far north, reducing the area of fertile land.

When the rain does come, it can be torrential, sudden and highly localised. Sometimes there is general rainfall over a large area, but more usually there is considerable variation within it. At one spot in Mali in 1990, for example, over half the annual rainfall of 400 mm fell in three storms on three different days [3]. The timing of such storms can determine whether an entire harvest will succeed or fail.

Despite its extremes and violent changes, the Sahelian environment is inherently stable and contains its own systems of correction. Much plant and animal life in the Sahelian environment is characterised by rapid reproduction and brief life cycles that make the most of the short rainy seasons, and many species are capable of sustaining long periods of dormancy.

The first substantial rains unleash sudden and massive activity. A haze of green appears over the surface of previously barren soil and covers the branches of apparently dead trees. Shoots push out of the parched soil and rapidly develop into vigorous plants. At night, there are animal noises unheard during the dry season. Insects appear from nowhere in unimaginable numbers and then just as mysteriously seem to disappear. Before the rains end, the feverish plant and animal activity begins to subside; the animals have had their young and the plants have set seed.

Rainfall determines the environment of the Sahel

It is clear that—fragile as it is—the Sahelian environment can support sustainable agricultural production and has in the past recovered from drought. The plant and animal life of the region has evolved to take full advantage of the environment's unpredictability and swift changes. Farmers and pastoralists, too, have evolved ways to sustain a productive relationship with the land.

Pastoralism

When things were at their worst, we heard there had been good rains at Essahwa. It was a long, difficult journey. When we arrived, we were happy because our journey had not been in vain—the land was very green and we rejoiced—then the *criquets* (locusts) came and ate all the vegetation! They even

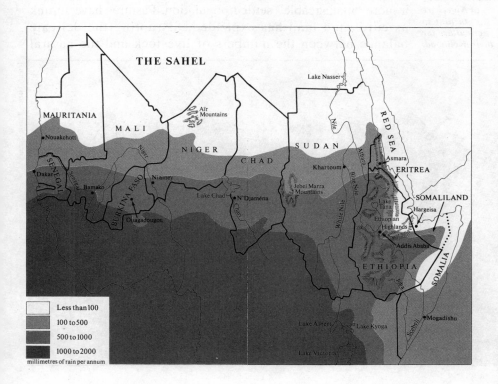

THE SAHEL

Less than 100
100 to 500
500 to 1000
1000 to 2000
millimetres of rain per annum

began to eat our tents and it was then that we had to start moving again. The only way we kept alive was by killing the camels that we had with us. We killed one camel and lived on that until it was gone and we had to kill another...all the time it was a race between us and the locusts to reach the vegetation first.

Fatimetou Mint Mohamed el Mokhtar, Mauritanian pastoralist

Pastoralism—looking after herds of cattle, sheep, goats and camels—has been practised in the Sahel for centuries. In this dossier, pastoralism is being used to include nomadism, in which wandering herders follow the rains and track down pockets of good pasture, and transhumance, which involves regular, seasonal migration between established grazing grounds. Both systems make skilled, rational use of marginal land, especially that in the northernmost fringe of the Sahel, where rainfall is lowest. Clearly, a system geared to making use of such limited resources is highly vulnerable: to trek long distances to pasture only to find it under attack by locusts, as the Mauritanian woman describes above, has major implications for the herders' survival.

Drought and changing social and economic practices mean many pastoralists, like these Tuareg in Niger, are turning to agriculture for their livelihood.

Today, pastoralism is under threat in many ways. Politicians and planners prefer more "modern" systems of production and a more "manageable" settled population. Pastures have shrunk as cultivated land has expanded, disrupting the delicate balance between the numbers of livestock and the natural

Jeremy Hartley/Panos Pictures

resources available. Drought has wiped out whole areas of grazing and dried up established watering places, conflict over dwindling resources has increased, and traditional alliances and trading routes have been disrupted. Younger generations want access to education, which implies settlement. More and more pastoralists are shifting to farming or combining both systems of production. Many others, particularly those who lost most or all their livestock to drought, are herding for wages from absentee owners, or moving to towns in search of work.

Farmers aim to reduce risk rather than maximise productivity

Settled farming

> We used to say that if you worked you could have everything you wanted. It was only those who did not pull their weight who found themselves struggling. Then a year came when locusts appeared from the skies and destroyed all our crops and we realised this statement was no longer true. Something more than hard work was necessary for survival.
> **Fatimé Achoumboule, Chad**

Farmers in the Sahel also have to make the most of the short periods of rapid growth that the rainy season provides. It gives most farmers, outside irrigated areas, one annual harvest. Millet and sorghum are the main staple crops. While arable farming in the region has always been a risky, low-investment, low-return system of production, it has been possible to live without major fears for survival, harvesting enough to build up stocks and develop some degree of security.

Over the last 25 to 30 years, this situation has been changing. Farmers' ability to make even minimal investments has declined. Intervening drought-free periods have not been sufficient for stocks to recover and people have had to sell their goods, including animals and agricultural equipment. This reduces their potential to farm in subsequent years and sets them on a downward spiral of impoverishment which is hard to reverse.

Farming in the Sahel has always been characterised by strategies which aim to reduce risk and get some harvest rather than to maximise productivity. The main threats to a successful harvest are the unpredictability of the rain and attack by locusts, grasshoppers or other pests. Resource-poor farmers have difficult decisions to make. For example, a farmer might decide not to spend money on pesticides when the threat of loss from drought is greater, because plants might be protected from some pest damage at great cost—only to fail from lack of water.

Drought has been one of the most devastating of the related factors contributing to the deteriorating environment in the Sahel, but at least dry conditions are unfavourable for locust activity. So just when there is a year or two of improved rainfall and the prospect of better yields, the threat of locust damage increases. Many a Sahelian farmer has suffered seeing their first good crop after years of poor rains, being ravaged by locusts or grasshoppers. A locust plague may thus be the final blow to families who have been surviving on a knife edge.

Among the most vulnerable of Sahelian farmers are the herders who have either changed to arable farming or increased their crop-growing activities as a consequence of losing many of their animals during the droughts. Some destitute herders, such as those who have settled in Tin Aica in Mali, have been given external assistance to start sedentary farming [4]. Most, though, have independently taken up some arable farming in order to reduce dependence on a single

Year	Country	Amount of crops eaten by the Desert Locust
1944	Libya	7,000,000 grapevines; 19% of total vine cultivation
1954	Sudan	55,000 tonnes of grain
1957	Senegal	16,000 tonnes of millet; 2,000 tonnes of other crops
1957	Guinea	6,000 tonnes of oranges
1958	Ethiopia	167,000 tonnes of grain, which is enough to feed a million people for a year
1962	India	4,000 hectares of cotton (value £300,000)

Year	Country	Value of crops destroyed by locusts (in £ sterling)	1986 value (in £ sterling)
1926-34	India	400,000 per year	6 million
1928-29	Kenya	300,000 per year	4.5 million
1953	Somalia (Southern Region)	600,000	
1954-55	Morocco	4,500,000 in a single season	40 million
1949-57	FAO estimate for only 12 out of 40 affected countires	1,500,000 per year; in 1955 over 5,000,000	45 million

Source: Adapted from the *Locust Handbook*, Natural Resources Institute, Chatham, UK, 1988

system of production [5]. Often they only have access to the most marginal land and have the least influence with plant protection staff.

When drought recedes, the threat of locust damage increases

The difference between the damage caused by drought and by locust attack is that generally, while some people obviously have greater resources to combat the results of drought, its effects are evenly spread. Locusts are often more selective; a swarm may devastate one farmer's fields and leave their neighbour's crops untouched. So it is difficult to estimate the relative importance of drought versus locust attack as a threat to Sahelian farmers, and even more difficult to establish accurate national figures for the social and economic damage caused by the insects. What is clear is that drought, while bad for farmers, reduces the threat of locusts. But when drought recedes, giving farmers the vital opportunity to harvest a surplus and build up stocks to survive the next lean period, locusts can destroy that opportunity: in other words, they attack at the worst possible time. To control these attacks could make a major difference to the survival of Sahelian farming.

Economic costs

> Locusts have caused an enormous amount of damage and it seems impossible to chase them away. Once they come into your field they do not leave until they have finished the crop, only leaving when there is nothing left to eat. Each one of us has to try to manage with what we have left. Our only thought is to find enough to eat: we can't contemplate being rich.
> **Bianhan Coulibaly, farmer, Mali**

> One year the grasshoppers were so bad we had to ask the state for assistance. They gave us powder to put on the land but it didn't kill the pests. The men also went to the *marabout* (local prayer leader/teacher) for help. He would beat his drums and cry to God but even this did not work. The only thing that was really effective was when the women themselves went to stand in the fields, from dawn to dusk, throwing stones and shouting to frighten off all the "intruders" who tried to snatch a bite to eat from our crops.
> **Mariam Madra, Chad**

There is plenty of anecdotal evidence of the terrible destruction of which locusts and grasshoppers are capable but few accurate estimates of damage caused and food lost. The *Locust Handbook* provides some examples, in the tables opposite. Partly as a result of the short-lived nature of the 1986-88 plague, and partly because of the perennial difficulty of obtaining accurate statistics, there are no overall figures for

There are crop losses during the plague of 1986-88.
few accurate   There are several reasons for the shortage of reliable data.
estimates of First, even normal yield data are not reliable for large areas of
food losses the Sahel. Much of the production is for subsistence and
therefore cannot be projected from market statistics. Many
areas of cultivation are remote and not visited by agriculture
staff or others who might record crop production. Production
is in any case extremely variable, not only between farms and
areas but also within fields. All these factors mean that staff
from the ministries of agriculture are often obliged to produce
production data by extrapolation, in precisely the kind of
situations in which generalisations are misleading.

In addition, locust damage is often indirect—for example,
affecting leaves only—and it is not easy to assess the extent to
which this will affect the grain harvest. Locusts and
grasshoppers may completely destroy young plants and if the
field is then abandoned, the loss is total. On the other hand,
older plants can sustain some loss of leaves without any effect
on the final grain yield.

Agricultural losses due to grasshoppers are similarly hard to
estimate but because they happen every year, with the
fluctuations in severity usually corresponding to the amount of
rainfall, they are cumulatively more significant than those
caused by locusts. A team working for a project covering a
small area of northwestern Mali produced figures showing
crop losses due to grasshoppers varying from 5% to 60-70%.
They also suggested that yields will be reduced because of
total loss of seedlings in 25% of the fields sown [6]. These
estimates were obtained by skilled personnel in an area that
they knew well, but such resources are rarely available.

Farmers' own estimates of loss are often subjective. They
may also be influenced, understandably, by how they think
their views will be used. They may exaggerate their losses if
they think this will help them obtain compensation or
assistance, or minimise them if they think they will be thought
of as bad farmers [7].

The people theoretically best able to collect loss data, the
pest control agents, are usually already working as hard as they
can. As Lukas Brader, former director of plant production and
protection, FAO, has pointed out, "...during control campaigns,
most plant protection staff are directly involved in control and
cannot therefore undertake crop damage assessments [8]."

The lack of hard data explains why calculations of food losses are often based on the insects' feeding habits—that is, what they could eat rather than what they have eaten. "A plague of desert locusts in Somaliland in 1957 was estimated to comprise sixteen thousand million locusts and weigh about 50,000 tons; and since locusts eat about their own weight in green food per day it is easy to see why they are so destructive," goes one typical description [9]. Powerful images like this—50,000 tonnes of locusts eating their weight in grain every day—explain why plagues arouse such fear of famine.

National statistics hide the real cost to individual farmers

The Russian-born British entomologist, Boris Uvarov, raises another difficulty with these kinds of generalisations: locust feeding patterns vary according to how active they are, and whether they are in groups or single. In his classic review of grasshopper and locust research, published in 1977, he concluded: "There are no quantitative data on the actual food consumption of either adults or hoppers...although this information is greatly needed for estimating their economic damage potential [10]."

More importantly, global or national statistics hide the real cost: the losses suffered by individual farmers. If, for example, crop losses in a particular area have been estimated at 30%, this might mean a generalised 30% level of infestation in the fields. What is much more likely, however, is that the insects have caused losses of nearer 100% in some fields, leaving others more or less untouched. An average figure thus disguises the fact that some people will harvest little or nothing that year, and will have to find some other means of survival. Generalised statistics are only really useful for gaining an impression of a situation and for comparing areas or years. They merely provide a starting point for asking questions.

Despite the elements of uncertainty, some things are clear: locusts have the potential to destroy crops and pasture on a massive scale—but the damage is intermittent and is not evenly distributed. Grasshoppers cause damage every year. Since losses from both are usually highly variable and hard to estimate, authenticated reliable data are rare—which adds to the difficulty of making decisions about the objectives and operation of control campaigns. Finally, the cost to those who suffer from grasshopper and locust attacks goes far beyond the loss of harvest or grazing land.

Social costs

[Grasshoppers] cause enormous damage, ravaging our crops and leaving nothing....My mother told me stories of some people becoming became so desperate that they gave children away in return for grain to eat.
Zouma Coulibaly, Malian farmer

Over the last 20 years, Sahelian farmers have been struggling to cope with increasingly fast social and economic change. Harvests have deteriorated, reserves dwindled and herds decreased, at the same time as social systems and kinship bonds have been disrupted and in some cases broken down.

The causes of social change are not simply that desertification, drought and pest damage are making farming increasingly untenable and forcing people to change their way of life. There has also been an increasing dislocation between the older and younger people, not least because many children now have access to formal education. This may increase a desire to work in urban areas, to take up a salaried job or to introduce a different approach to farming or herding. There has been "a loss of cultural continuity. Traditional knowledge is considered 'out of date' by young villagers as well as outsiders.....[there has been a] breakdown of traditional relationships between groups: adults and children, sedentary farmers, pastoralists and agro-pastoralists, men and women [11]." And as resources become scarce, relationships break

Just when there is plenty of rain and the promise of good yields like these, insect activity increases and so does the threat of plagues.

Ron Giling/Panos Pictures

Urban migration has increased throughout the Sahel. Women and older people are left in the villages, trying to make a living from the arid land.

down further and conflict develops between village, ethnic group, region and even nation [12].

One social consequence of the deteriorating situation in the Sahel has been increased migration from rural areas; in some cases this is seasonal, but increasingly it is more or less permanent. It is usually young men who migrate first, which reduces the labour available for farming. The migrants will try to find work and send remittances home but this is not always possible. Increasingly, older people, women and children are left in the villages, trying to coax sufficient harvests from the soil.

> When I was young, men and women used to farm together in the same field. Now the men spend so much time travelling in search of work elsewhere....Our men are courageous—they go as far as Nigeria to find work—but sometimes I feel it is the women, who stay here with the children, not knowing where they are going to find the next meal, who are stronger.
> **Mariam Madra, Chad**

Declining productivity means farmers are cultivating three times as much land

Devastating crop losses from locusts and grasshoppers after years of drought may force whole families to abandon farming and migrate to Sahelian towns. Often they end up living on the urban fringes, unable to find work. This is not only a personal tragedy for the families concerned but has wider social consequences for the already overstretched urban areas. Perhaps even more importantly, this migration has serious implications for national food production. Urgent efforts are needed to help stabilise the marginal rural populations so that they can support themselves, and in years of good rainfall produce a surplus. To promote the repopulation of rural areas once they have been abandoned will be far more difficult than to stem the current drift.

Changing farm systems

> When I was young...plants, men and animals lived together in harmony. The soils were fertile and productive. Then the rain gradually petered out. We began to cut the trees down and lose respect for our old customs....Today the environment is sick, the soils are poor and hard, and the trees are dead, scorched by the sun....To make up for poor harvests, larger areas of land have been given over to cultivation. We can only afford to leave the land fallow for one or two years, compared to four or five years in the past.
> **Obo Koné, Mali**

One response to the worsening climatic conditions has been a change in farming practices: increased sowing of short-cycle varieties, less rotation of crops and reduced fallow periods. These are logical responses to the uncertainties of Sahelian farming but they tend to increase the longer-term risks by weakening an already fragile agricultural system.

Sahelian farmers, as already stated, have always worked on the basis that some loss is inevitable and so try to minimise the risk of total harvest failure. Today, because of declining productivity, this means that many farmers are cultivating three times as much land, sometimes more, in the hope of harvesting enough for their subsistence. In general, they have also tried to diversify within their production systems. There is a tendency towards more mixed farming and more integration of arable and animal farming. Farmers may grow a wider range of crops and varieties, and spread these over different fields with a range of sowing dates. The greater diversity means more likelihood of at least some production of some crop.

Sowing seed at staggered intervals means that if one sowing

fails because of poor rainfall at a crucial period, others may succeed. Sowing as large an area as possible may help, since rain can be so localised. Sowing different varieties means conditions unsuitable for one may produce a harvest from another. New varieties of sorghum and millet which require a shorter growing season have been developed, but agricultural extension services remain inadequate and farmers often cannot afford the costs of introducing new technologies, fertilisers or other inputs. But today, labour is probably the most important constraint, a factor which has particular implications for methods of locust and grasshopper control that involve farmer participation (see Chapter Six).

Today, labour is the most important constraint

Traditional control methods

To try and control the numbers of these insects we used to dig holes in which the grasshoppers entered. As soon as a few had gathered we would cover the hole with earth and bury them. This is one of the only ways we knew of killing them.
Hanzoun Dabon, Mali

Locusts, which have plagued us four times in my life, have been responsible for endless devastation. To try to control their numbers we hit them with sticks and build fires. We wear sandals with hard soles to trample on them—this together with the smoke from the fire may eventually chase them away. Thankfully the state has...shown us how to protect our fields and chase away the insects by digging trenches and using metal sheets.
Obo Koné, Mali

Looking back on my life, one of the most distressing times was when the locusts swooped down on the fields. They plagued us for about five years, although we tried to frighten them off with sticks and sheets of metal. We tried to bury them alive in holes in the ground. We even trampled on them, squashing their bodies with our sandals. In those days we planted *pois de terre* (groundnuts) as these were the only grains that were resistant to locusts.
Se'e Dembélé, Mali

Most traditional methods of pest control used by farmers tend towards risk reduction rather than risk avoidance, the same approach as that employed to protect harvests from poor weather. The intercropping of sorghum and millet is an obvious example. Locusts and grasshoppers seem to prefer millet; only when they are very hungry or if there is no choice will they eat sorghum leaves or grain. Sowing millet varieties that produce particularly hairy heads can also reduce losses

*Villagers
dig trenches in
which to bury
locust hoppers.*

USAID *Crop Protection clip art book*

from locust attacks.

Other methods of control include chasing insects out of crops, burying young hoppers in loose sand, ploughing up egg-pod fields, driving cattle into vegetation that is heavily infested, setting fire to the grass in which the pests are found, and attracting them at night to fires in which they are then destroyed. At best, these methods achieve some damage limitation. A number of such methods used together or in conjunction with chemical spraying could do more.

Barriers, made from sheets of galvanised iron or plywood, can be used to intercept bands of hoppers and then direct them into pits or trenches where they are destroyed. This method is only worthwhile against large mobile bands and where there are the materials and plenty of people to carry out the considerable work of erecting the barriers. In practice, rural depopulation means that there are often shortages of labour and, in addition, the areas where the hopper bands occur and the vulnerable crops grow are vast. Thus this method, while environmentally safe, is unlikely to have any large-scale impact. This is not to devalue its potential in local situations.

A century-old law

Locust control in the Sudan was carried out in the past in observance of the rule of law. Government officials were empowered to call upon every person capable of labour to assist in the destruction of locusts and locust eggs. In the archives of the Ministry of Agriculture in Khartoum, is a copy of the Locusts Destruction Ordinance of 1907, which was legislated by the British. The law empowered "Governors, District Commissioners, Assistant District Commissioners, Mamurs, Omdas, Sheiks and any person authorised by them for purposes of destroying locusts and locust eggs, to enter upon any land and dig, plough and turn over the soil, erect screens, dig pits, burn scrub and do all such other thing as may be expedient for the aforesaid purpose".

The law further stipulated that "any person who after being called on to assist in the destruction neglects to do so, shall be liable to imprisonment for a term not exceeding 30 days or to a fine not exceeding LS2."

Mohamed Hisham, Sudan

A complex web

A number of different forces are operating in the Sahel, combining to undermine the development possibilities of the world's poorest region. Drought, environmental degradation, social change and tensions, unwise development, conflict and war are all related, and all feed upon each other. And as the resource base continues to deteriorate, the potential for conflict is increasing. Locust damage is just one factor among many, and one which only intermittently seizes the imagination and forces international action. The cycle of short periods of frenzied control operations and massive expenditure interspersed with long periods of inactivity—which resembles the pattern of annual growth of Sahelian plant and insect life—has done little to increase the security of the Sahelian farmer. Moreover, many pests, and grasshoppers in particular, cause continual damage on a chronic if less dramatic scale. By ignoring the long-term costs of this damage, donor agencies and governments are contributing to the deterioration of the harsh but nevertheless potentially sustainable environment of the Sahel.

Some argue that because locust swarms have tended to affect poorer millet farmers more than others, the losses sustained in national terms are relatively insignificant. But these farmers are the least able to carry such losses, so they become the landless poor and as such represent an important cost to their country. A further flaw in that argument is that locusts do not always only affect the more marginal lands and

Locusts as a source of food

Locusts were another delicacy. When they came to stand on a tree, we would dig a hole under the tree in which we would light a fire. The smoke would overcome the locusts and they would fall into the hole. The next morning after the fire had gone out the people would take them, grind them into a powder and then eat them. We use them to treat tuberculosis and pneumonia. We say that since locusts eat from all kinds of trees they must be the cure for all diseases, since there is a tree to cure every ailment.

Ghwaya Mint Ayed, Mauritanian pastoralist

Locusts can contribute significantly to the human diet. It is suggested that consumption of 150 fried locusts per day would provide a person's daily protein requirements, and 10% of daily calorie needs. They are also eaten by poultry and all categories of domestic animals and wildlife [13].

Since locusts are a common food source, the danger of people being poisoned by pesticide residues is a real one. In Niger in 1987, there were reports of people becoming seriously ill from eating locusts and grasshoppers. Samples taken from Niamey marketplace and analysed were contaminated with the pesticides dieldrin and BHC [14].

Incidents of poisoning can be reduced by using radio programmes and crop protection agents to alert the public to impending spray campaigns, and by raising awareness of the precautions which should be taken over affected crops and insects. People need also to be warned (as was done in Mauritania and other Sahelian countries during the 1988 upsurge) of the possibility of contaminated grasshoppers and locusts being imported from other areas or countries where pesticides have been used.

poorer farmers. They have the potential to devastate crops on a scale far more significant nationally—and have done so in the past. The key point is that the loss of agricultural production from locust and grasshopper attacks does have a direct and adverse effect on the social fabric and stability of Sahelian countries.

CHAPTER 3

Locusts and grasshoppers

The Sahelian ecosystem, characterised by annual cycles of extended dry periods and inactivity interspersed with brief times of rapid growth and reproduction, has a stability of its own. For example, the need for insects to reproduce rapidly and on a large scale, so that some offspring may survive, means that sizes of populations undergo dramatic changes. If only a few offspring survive, then the numbers may remain fairly stable, but if a good proportion find favourable conditions the ensuing rate of increase can be enormous. Similarly, adverse conditions can mean that numbers decline very rapidly.

There is then, a self-regulatory mechanism, even if the numbers involved are very high or very low. It is this kind of environment, one of extremes, that produces plagues—and the locust is perfectly adapted to it, able to modify its behaviour according to its needs and the prevailing conditions. Its numbers can increase at an extraordinary rate, but the decline can be equally rapid. Locusts and grasshoppers are close biological relatives, belonging to the same insect family: *Acrididae.* In terms of successful adaptation to conditions in the Sahel, the important factors for grasshoppers and locusts are their capacity to reproduce fast, the flexible organisation of the life cycle, and their ability to undergo "gregarisation" and migrate (see p30). This last characteristic, essentially limited to locusts, makes them particularly significant pests. When numbers are too high for available resources, the Desert Locust's ability to move on in a cohesive group—often over huge distances—is clearly an effective survival strategy in an area where vegetation may be patchy and widely distributed.

Migration is, however, only one possible survival mechanism for locusts and grasshoppers in the Sahel. Some species adapt to unfavourable conditions by becoming dormant, often for long periods. For example, while some species spend the dry season as adults, others, such as the

Senegalese Grasshopper, survive this period as eggs in a resting state called "diapause". The eggs do not develop until the diapause is broken by some environmental trigger. If successive seasons are unfavourably dry, the eggs may continue to remain dormant.

Overall, flexibility is a key characteristic of these insects' behaviour patterns, which obviously maximises their ability to respond to an uncertain and changeable environment.

Life cycle

All grasshoppers and locusts in the Sahel are capable of dramatic population increases. A reasonable calculation is that an insect laying about 100 eggs could produce 10 offspring— and these could become mature adults, capable of producing another generation, in as little as two to three months. This fast rate of increase is not special to these pests; many other types of insect are capable of comparable feats.

Similarly, all locusts and grasshoppers are capable of living solitary lives, as most other insect species are. Where locusts do differ is that when they proliferate, it is not just their large numbers that cause problems; they actually change their behaviour in a way that constitutes a greater threat. Dense aggregations of most insects simply disperse after a time but dense populations of locusts tend to become gregarious, keeping together in compact bands or swarms and migrating to new areas (see box overleaf).

Terminology

This ability to become gregarious is for many scientists the distinguishing factor between grasshoppers and locusts. However, there are a few "aggregating" grasshoppers which behave in a similar fashion—multiplying rapidly and producing swarms—and so the distinction between the two kinds of insect is sometimes misleading, and is part of the reason why grasshoppers have not been taken as seriously as pests as they deserve. The Senegalese Grasshopper is in a particularly ambiguous position, since it does aggregate and migrate over considerable distances. It is almost unique in getting as close as it does to behaving like a locust.

Currently the word "locust" in the Sahel usually refers to only two species long recognised as migratory pests: the African Migratory Locust and the Desert Locust. The former seems to have gone into permanent recession in its primary outbreak area, the floodplains of the Niger delta in Mali,

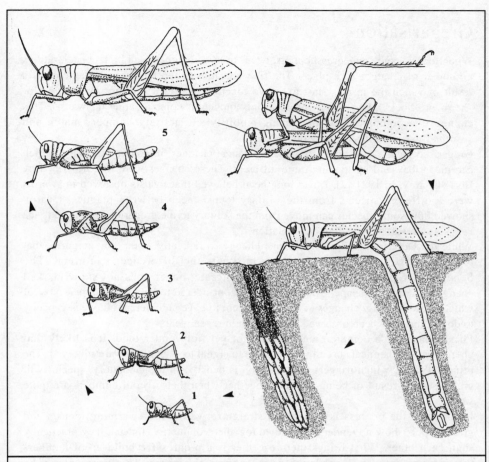

The life cycle of all species of grasshopper and locust consists of three stages: eggs, hoppers and adults. Eggs hatch into hoppers, primarily during the rainy season. Hoppers periodically shed their skins, usually five times, as they grow. The successive growth stages are known as "instars". It is during these non-flying stages that the insects are easiest to control, although the biggest challenge is to locate and effectively target the populations which need control. After the last moult, the immature adults have developed wings and are able to fly. Colour changes sometimes occur when adults become sexually mature. The Desert Locust can produce a new generation in about three months, while the Senegalese Grasshopper takes two months.

probably because of environmental changes brought about by drought and increased land use. Sporadic outbreaks still occur in the Lake Chad basin. A third species, the Tree Locust, does swarm but is less mobile and much less of a crop pest. Indeed, it is "categorized by some acridologists among aggregating grasshoppers because of [its] poor swarming behavior [1]". Tree Locusts, however, are recognised as an important pest in Chad and particularly Sudan, where in some years they inflict serious damage to gum-producing acacias and fruit trees.

Gregarisation

When locusts, and some grasshoppers, occur in large numbers and high concentrations a number of changes take place. The first and most important is in behaviour, as a result of which the insects start to crowd together or gregarise ("grex" is Latin for "herd" or "flock"). Hoppers will form bands and adults come together in swarms. This change is accompanied by increasing mobility and activity: hoppers march and swarms fly, sometimes for long distances.

Gregarised locusts also undergo marked physical changes, in colour and shape, which can mean they end up looking quite different. These changes were first described by Boris Uvarov, in 1921 [2]. It had long been believed that locusts observed in swarms were a different species from the solitary locusts seen between plagues. Uvarov showed how some species can move from the solitary to the gregarious phase and vice versa, as a result of crowding and isolation.

While the Desert and Migratory Locust change so radically when they gregarise that they look like two different species, in others the difference is minimal. The Senegalese Grasshopper does swarm and migrate, but it does not show marked changes in colour or shape. Consequently it is considered to be a grasshopper, most of which show no phase changes at all. Some seem to have an inherent but weak capacity to do so, and have been observed to gregarise in recent years.

Phase change is a complex mechanism, not yet fully understood. It is likely that pheromones—chemicals used by the insects to signal to each other—are involved. The principal factor which triggers gregarisation is density: in the laboratory, species will gregarise as a result of being crowded together when their overall numbers are quite small.

In the field the process is rather less straightforward. Non-swarming locusts and grasshoppers show no tendency to crowd together voluntarily. Indeed, they practically shun each other. What brings them together is a progressive build-up of numbers through breeding and/or through arrivals from elsewhere. This process may be hastened by the drying out of vegetation which causes suitable habitats to gradually shrink in size.

Eventually a threshold density is reached and the insects begin to respond to the situation and actively crowd together in ever increasing numbers. The end result of the process is the formation of flying swarms and marching bands. This may mark the start of a serious outbreak, although the extent to which they can maintain their cohesion in the face of disruptive environmental conditions depends on the degree of gregarisation they have achieved, their overall numbers (the higher the better) and how soon they meet the right conditions to breed again.

Should they succeed in staying together and breeding, the next generation will start with a higher level of gregarisation, partly because of the density of numbers but also because some phase attributes are hereditary. Thus the process can be continued from one generation to another as long as numbers and densities remain high. Conversely, gregarised locusts revert to their solitary state if the swarm breaks up and they become scattered.

All other species in the Sahel are conventionally referred to as grasshoppers. However, it would be useful to distinguish between those grasshoppers that can form highly mobile swarms as locusts do, and those that remain fairly close to where they hatch. The more mobile species are also the ones which produce more than one generation annually: the more generations in a year, the greater the size of the population and the damage it can inflict.

Before 1989 it might also have been possible to distinguish clearly between those grasshoppers that can cause a great deal of crop damage and those that rarely have such impact. However, the huge upsurge in numbers of usually unimportant species, for example *Kraussella* (see p33), and the damage that they cause, means that an increasing number of species of grasshoppers have achieved pest status in the Sahel. Of over 200 species in the western Sahel, some 10 or 12 have been noted as causing significant crop damage.

A false distinction?

As already stated, grasshoppers and locusts are closely related and are primarily distinguished by their behaviour rather than appearance. Locusts form marching bands or flying swarms and migrate together in these dense formations. It is when they are in this gregarious phase that locusts represent the greatest

Locusts fly off, having picked clean an acacia, Sudan. The exact economic costs of plagues are hard to establish but Sudan's fruit trees and gum-producing acacias have been seriously damaged in recent years.

Mike Goldwater/Network

Jeremy Hartley/Panos Pictures

One of the many species of grasshopper which regularly devastate crops in the Sahel. The severity of grasshopper attacks varies with the rainfall, but even in dry years some crop loss occurs, whereas locusts do little or no damage in times of drought.

danger to agriculture. Most grasshoppers do not aggregate and migrate in this way, even when very numerous. Grasshoppers are also likely to breed in or close to cropland. The Desert Locust, by contrast, usually breeds in the remote areas of the Sahara desert well away from cropland, which is not threatened by this species except during plagues.

These differences in behaviour and in breeding patterns have major implications for control strategies and require different tactics. For example, locust swarms, while highly destructive, do at least form a clear target, whereas grasshopper bands move together in a much more loosely organised way. But because they breed close to cultivated land, grasshoppers are more easily located and treated, and farmers can usefully participate in this task. By the time swarms of Desert Locusts reach cropland, they have been developing their numbers in inaccessible breeding areas for over a year. Prevention is therefore a particularly relevant strategy for these insects, but is a task for specialised control units.

Finally, locusts are notorious for their capacity for destruction; grasshoppers have no such notoriety. But, as Sahelian farmers know to their cost, this last distinction is a false one. While grasshoppers may not have caught the imagination of chroniclers of plagues as locusts have, they too devastate crops and rangeland. In fact, over the last five years they have caused more damage in the Sahel than locusts. Locust damage tends to be irregular, largely unpredictable, widespread when it does occur, and is usually attributable to an upsurge of one particular species. Grasshopper outbreaks more often involve several species and cause chronic damage at the local level every year.

There would be little problem with any ambiguity in the distinction between grasshoppers and locusts if they were both equally perceived as threats to the livelihoods of people in the Sahel. While locusts in the Sahel have long been recognised as major crop pests, and regional and international organisations for their control came into existence around the 1940s, there is scarcely any official record of grasshoppers as pests or any mention in the annals of crop protection—until the 1970s. This could be because such damage as was inflicted by grasshoppers, and other pests, was tolerated as part and parcel of habitual poor yields in the Sahel.

With the advent of worsening drought in the 1960s, and increasing famine, the impact of pest damage began to be felt more acutely and attitudes changed. In 1970 OCLALAV, with responsibility for preventive control of the Desert Locust and grain-eating birds, was pressurised into controlling grasshoppers and treated 10,500 hectares. More treatment was carried out the next year, but in 1974, when rainfall returned to normal, a grasshopper plague occurred on an unprecedented scale, spearheaded by the Senegalese Grasshopper. OCLALAV then treated 194,000 hectares but this did little to avert devastating crop losses. A donors' meeting recommended the

Sahelian grasshoppers and locusts [3]

Locusts

Schistocerca gregaria	Desert Locust
Locusta migratoria migratorioides	Migratory Locust
Anacridium melanorhodon	Tree Locust

Aggregating grasshoppers

Oedaleus senegalensis	Senegalese Grasshopper
Aiolopus simulatrix	Sudan Plague Locust
Zonocerus variegatus	Variegated Grasshopper

Other grasshoppers

Kraussaria angulifera	
Hieroglyphus daganensis	Rice Grasshopper
Diablolocatantops axillaris	
Cataloipus cymbiferus	
Kraussella amabile	
Cryptocatantops haemorrhoidalis	
Ornithacris cavroisi	

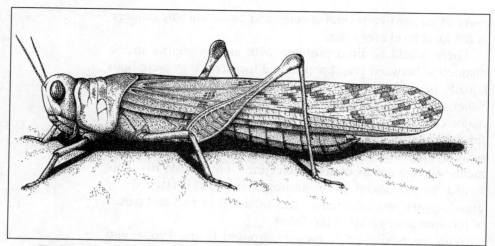

The Desert Locust, *Schistocerca gregaria*
diversion of some of the funds allocated to the then Office for the Sahelian Relief Operations, and in 1975 about one million hectares were treated—at the time, the largest such operation conducted in the Sahel. This might have helped the subsequent decline in grasshopper numbers, although sporadic outbreaks occurred throughout the later 1970s. There was then a period of quiescence during the drought of the early 1980s, followed by an outbreak in 1985 when rainfall returned to near normal.

The infestations the following year, 1986, were again of plague proportions and this insect has caused serious damage every year subsequently. A good number of other grasshopper species have also caused considerable damage, frequently swarming just like locusts. It should be acknowledged that the damage caused by these outbreaks was magnified because of the expansion of cropland which had taken place. Another possible factor is that increased use of pesticides may have disproportionately affected the natural enemies of grasshoppers and so disrupted the balance between them.

Changes in land use do influence the distribution of locusts and grasshoppers—for example, when irrigation brings moisture to previously dry areas and natural vegetation is reduced or gives way to cultivated crops. *A Plague of Locusts* cites the fact that "the African Migratory Locust today is behaving more like a nongregarious grasshopper due to the breakup of its habitat in Mali....[while] the Variegated Grasshopper, a minor nuisance in the 1930s, became a major problem in the 1970s following widespread forest clearing for coffee production in the Ivory Coast...", which created

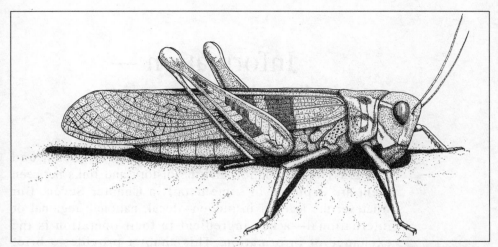

The Senegalese Grasshopper, *Oedaleus senegalensis*

environmental conditions in which the pest flourished [4].

Another reason for grasshoppers retaining a relatively innocuous image is that the principal witnesses of the recent outbreaks have been farmers and local plant protection staff. There isn't the unifying response of large areas being affected by the same problem, as there is with a locust plague, and so the seriousness of the damage is not communicated to the policy-influencing heads of national, regional and international control organisations, ministers of agriculture or donors' advisors. Even national-level pest management researchers do not focus sufficiently on grasshoppers as a priority pest. Cost-benefit information is lacking.

While improving the sources of information collection will make a major contribution to more effective decision-making about grasshopper and locust control, there will always be variable elements to complicate the picture. Changing weather conditions will always affect insect activity. And no one species is likely to dominate indefinitely because of the dynamics between pests and their predators. For example, as the numbers of grasshoppers increased, so did those of the blister beetle, whose larvae feed on grasshopper eggs. Over a season or two, the beetles flourished to such an extent that they in turn became serious pests, as the adult beetles' food includes such food crops as millet and cowpeas. However, as the number of grasshoppers was reduced, the number of beetles began to diminish again. Locusts and grasshoppers cannot be dealt with in isolation but need to be seen against the whole spectrum of Sahelian pests and their habitats.

CHAPTER 4

Information —
the vital ingredient

A number of institutions are involved in locust and grasshopper control, and the history and links between them are explored in some detail in Chapter Seven. But whatever the level of institution—local, national, regional or international—a key ingredient in their operation is the exchange of information. This chapter provides a brief overview of methods of collecting information. It also describes some of the practical constraints on communicating information and using it to predict and control outbreaks.

The importance of preparedness

National crop protection services in the Sahel suffer a number of limitations on their ability to react to situations with speed and flexibility, not least difficulties in communicating information and transporting resources across huge distances.

Transport in the region has severe limitations. It is more difficult to fly to different areas within the Sahel than it is to reach them from Europe. Mali, Niger, Burkina Faso and Chad are all land-locked. Imports have to come by air or sea to a neighbouring country and then be moved by rail or road to their final destination. Distances are often enormous and roads are bad. During the rains many become impassable, defeating even four-wheel-drive cars. There are few properly trained mechanics and spare parts are in short supply and expensive. When, in 1988, Japan gave a number of Mitsubishi Pajero cars to the Malian plant protection service through the Food and Agriculture Organization (FAO), there was not a single spare part for them in the country. Britain's Overseas Development Administration, to its credit, followed up its own gift of Land Rovers with a large shipment of spare parts, specified by the Malian service. During the rainy season, airstrips may become impossible for larger aircraft to use, although helicopters are not so limited.

Transporting large quantities of equipment, fuel and pesticides under these conditions is a nightmare. It is vital to

George Popov

Transporting pesticides and equipment during the rains can be almost impossible. Vehicles get stuck in the mud and landing strips become unusable.

have the resources necessary for a locust campaign in place before the rains begin. Although staff cannot predict exactly where the resources will be most useful, waiting until they can be targeted more accurately may well mean it is too late to move them about at all.

A drum of pesticide to be used in August has to be moved up country by May at the latest. This means it has to be in the country no later than April, which in turn means being dispatched from its country of origin in January. Yet firm predictions of campaign requirements eight months ahead are impossible. The donor either has to risk air-freight costs later in the year or contribute on the basis of guesswork, which can lead to over-supply and later problems of disposal and pollution (see p60). An attempt to resolve this problem is the "pesticide bank", along the lines of one created by the European Community during the last plague, in which a reserve of pesticides is kept at a site from where it can in theory be readily mobilised.

All these factors mean that, while plant and insect life in the Sahel are able to adapt to changing conditions with speed, the plant protection services have immense obstacles to overcome in order to achieve any such flexibility. The key to a successful locust campaign therefore depends on being well prepared.

This in turn depends on the efficient gathering and interpretation of information.

Collecting Information

For species that pass the dry season as eggs, the first point of information is the immediate past. Knowing where concentrations of adults were located at the end of the last season may indicate the principle egg-laying sites and thus where new populations will emerge when the next rains begin. At present it is not possible to make the same predictions for species that pass the dry season as adults. However, it is clear that each season's control programme should end with comprehensive reporting of the pest situation. Some of the information will be of immediate use in planning next season's campaign and some will be useful in the longer term. A regional perspective and regional coordination are necessary for efficient data collection.

Egg-pod surveys

The most basic stage of gathering information on the distribution of grasshoppers is the egg-pod survey. Digging or scratching away the top layer of the soil reveals the grasshopper egg-pods. It is a time-consuming exercise, requires some training, and has been most effective with the Senegalese Grasshopper and a few other species. Given the huge areas to be covered, it is clearly impossible to carry out a scientifically accurate survey in this manner. Surveyors rely on their own and the farmers' knowledge of where the grasshoppers have been, and the kind of terrain and soil that the insects prefer for egg-laying. The survey is thus, in effect, an estimate of densities of egg-pods in areas that are reasonably accessible and judged to be likely breeding grounds. In some areas, villages are paid according to the number of egg-pods dug up, although the value of this approach for gathering survey information is debatable.

In spite of the frequently unscientific nature of the survey, the results can be used to assess and compare the potential threat of early season damage in different areas. In recent years in Mali, egg-pod surveys have been combined with egg-pod excavation and destruction operations conducted by farmers. These have helped to reduce, at a local level, numbers of *Kraussaria*, *Hieroglyphus* and *Cataloipus*, which lay eggs in dense concentrations at the base of trees and bushes around

George Popov

fields. Identifying laying sites also helps with the location and treatment of emerging hoppers, but once adults have appeared, predicting and protecting areas at risk becomes much more difficult.

Digging away the soil and taking samples in order to identify the preferred egg-laying sites of different species of grasshopper, Mali.

In 1989, there were severe attacks by a wide range of species of grasshoppers that had not been predicted by the preceding dry season's egg-pod surveys. This was probably because the survey was not designed to cover all possible species, nor those which pass the dry season as adults. Egg-pod surveying is generally not practical for the Desert Locust, because it breeds continuously and the period of egg development is so brief.

Ground surveys

Most surveying is carried out by "scouts" in cars, who can cover considerable areas if they are prepared to camp out for long periods. They have time to carry out careful inspections, and to talk to local farmers. Costs are manageable and the main restrictions are the state of the roads and vehicles, and fuel supplies. High-frequency transceiver radios are essential in order to disseminate the information collected.

Ground surveys cannot be claimed to provide totally objective records. It is impossible to survey by vehicle in a systematic way, for this would mean, for example, driving along a grid or transect and surveying at predetermined

The costs intervals. As with egg-pod surveys, the results are biased
of aerial towards finding insects in accessible places, in areas which the
surveys are scouts recognise as likely habitats, aided by information from
hard to aerial and satellite surveys.
justify

Aerial surveys

Flying low in a fixed-wing aircraft, a trained observer can get a
quick overview of a large area, verify indications of favourable
vegetation, and help direct survey and control efforts both in
the air and on the ground. Helicopters are the ideal means for
surveying, since the scout can also verify on the ground the
nature of the vegetation, and rapidly assess insect infestations
and the effectiveness of treatments. But the costs of such
surveys, at about US$5,000 per day, are astronomical, hard to
justify economically, and clearly beyond the scope of most
Sahelian national budgets. In addition, the aircraft need to be
supported on the ground by vehicles carrying crew and fuel,
which restricts their range.

Satellite surveys

Grasshopper and locust control involves a great deal of
unpredictability, not least because the weather is the key agent
that affects insect activity. Meteorologists use a range of
sources for recognising and recording weather patterns but the
scope of their work has been revolutionised by the use of
observations from satellites.

Everything depends on rain. A general idea of the extent
and intensity of rains can be predicted from the movements of
the Inter-tropical Convergence Zone (ITCZ), which seem to
correlate with the temperature of the surface of the oceans.
Work on producing useful predictions for specific areas rather
than for the Sahel as a whole is continuing, but is still some
way from delivering authoritative and accepted advice. An
unusual sequence of events conspired to undermine this work
in 1988 when predictions of an exceptionally dry year were
followed by the highest rainfall for over 20 years.

Although the reasons for this failure are now understood, it
was a setback to the credibility of the forecasting. Methods for
recording the weather are also inadequate. This is not to
devalue, but to emphasise the difficulties of the work of the
Centre for Application of Agrometeorology and Hydrology for
the Sahel (AGRHYMET) and the other data collection
services. Even industrialised countries, with all their resources,
have not yet developed faultless weather forecasting methods.

In the Sahel, the irregular and localised nature of the rainfall means that satellite technology has particular value for those responsible for determining whether certain areas are producing the vegetation which creates ideal breeding sites for locusts, and which attracts the mobile adults. *Satellite observations have great potential*

At present, the links between observations of the weather over the Sahel and grasshopper and locust biology are tenuous but the regional scope offered by satellite observations has great potential. Currently, the use of Meteosat images of temperature are used to create pictures of cloud cover and these can be interpreted to give indications of rainfall. The reception station and other necessary technology are relatively cheap and the system can provide frequent maps of areas where there is a high probability of rain.

At present, these data can only be useful if they are compared with knowledge on the ground to identify areas that need to be surveyed in more detail. The observations would be particularly useful early in the season if they recorded areas of rainfall undetected by other methods. If these areas coincided with potentially high populations of insects and vulnerable crops, then further assessment of risk could be undertaken.

Satellite imagery also provides a Normative Difference Vegetation Index on a 10-day basis. These so called "greenness" maps are produced regularly with USAID support at AGRHYMET in Niger and transmitted to the Sahelian states. Their resolution is one square kilometre and they are unlikely to miss significant vegetation, except that growing in the narrowest wadis or in areas covered by cloud, which is rarely a problem. Single maps are difficult to interpret in detail, since they indicate states of vegetation on a scale which does not easily relate to the situation on the ground. A sequence of maps is more useful, because it provides an idea of the growth of vegetation. In other words, these maps are most useful for purposes of comparison rather than for gaining an idea of the "greenness" itself.

Greenness maps are particularly useful for monitoring the conditions in the recession breeding grounds of the Desert Locust (see map overleaf). An experienced scout, familiar with the geography, can readily identify which particular wadis have "greened", are likely to offer suitable breeding conditions, and need checking for the presence of locusts. However, there is a need to enhance the greening at the lower end of the scale

The distribution of the Desert Locust

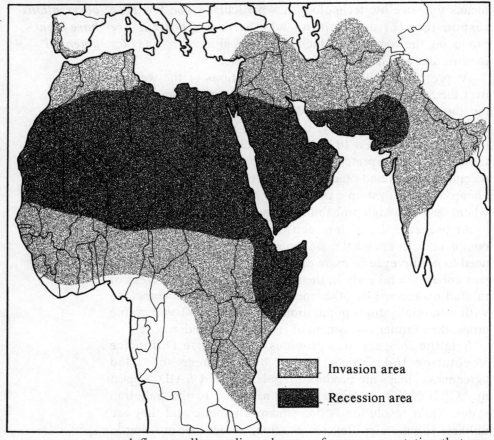

Invasion area

Recession area

to define smaller wadis and areas of sparser vegetation that can also make suitable breeding areas.

Current difficulties with satellite technology for locust control include access to information and timing. The length of time required for a patch of vegetation to grow and be detected on a map—and for that information to reach those who could use it for control decision-making—could be as long as the insects need to develop into threatening populations. There is also some concern that very slight plant growth may escape detection, while providing sufficient food for locust populations to develop. It seems likely that this problem could be overcome by adaptation of the technology to the Sahelian context. Again, the greenness maps are only valuable at present when used in conjunction with other data. Geographic information systems (GIS) technology offers excellent opportunities to merge the various "layers" of data.

Managing and Interpreting Information

The use of satellite intelligence in locust control has not yet been fully checked and calibrated against the reality on the ground during major outbreaks. Refinements and modifications over the next few years will undoubtedly make it much more useful for the prevention of Desert Locust outbreaks. Application of this technology to grasshopper control has hardly begun.

Ultimately, meteorological information from any one source—satellites, weather stations, survey teams, farmers, herders—is unlikely on its own to provide an adequate picture of the development of crops, natural vegetation or pests, but an intelligent combination of data from a variety of sources could significantly contribute to better control.

In fact, all relevant information—not only the weather and vegetation, but also regional and local accounts of pest developments, movements and treatments, and the status and distribution of equipment and supplies—has to be coordinated and interpreted together. The regional organisations used a radio network to collect information from local survey teams and national centres. The information was then synthesised and disseminated in two directions: to field staff, who made immediate practical use of it, and to donors, governments, FAO and other UN organisations. The current attempts to provide a two-way information service are described in Chapter Seven (p78).

Radio remains a crucial element in information exchange, because one institutional legacy from the colonial period in the Sahel is a communication system with a number of characteristics hampering locust control. It is, for example, easier to telephone from a capital city in the Sahel to one in Europe, than to a regional town or even another Sahelian capital.

Moreover, internal postal services are slow and unreliable. Thus the most common way to send urgent communications is over the national radio, which has a programme devoted entirely to small announcements. National organisations and even ministries make official announcements by this method. Getting news from the regions back to the capital is even more difficult, yet such flows of information are particularly important for locust and grasshopper control: the collection of observations from a wide area is essential for successful pest management. Short wave radio is thus a major means of communication between outlying bases and central and regional headquarters, and all field operators have to be proficient in the use and maintenance of radio receivers.

Mathematical models

PRIFAS (Projet de Recherche Inter-disciplinaire Français sur les Acridiens du Sahel) in Montpellier, France, has developed a prototype mathematical population model of the Senegalese Grasshopper (*Oedaleus senegalensis* or OSE). By means of microcomputer programmes, Biomodèle OSE uses existing information (field observations of the pest and meteorological data) to predict its distribution, geographically and over time, throughout the life cycle. Computers have been installed in the headquarters of several Sahelian plant protection services. The model could prove useful either in confirming ground observations, filling in gaps in information or, where predictions differ markedly, in defining where extra surveys are necessary. It is an important development as it shows that use can be made of already available, rudimentary information to refine control operations [1]. If progress can be made with control of the Senegalese Grasshopper, breeding over a huge area which seasonal and annual fluctuations make hard to define, it bodes well for all control operations. PRIFAS is also well on the way to developing a Desert Locust biomodel.

CHAPTER 5

In the field

After surveying and data collection come the decisions over treatment and control. The next chapter outlines the different methods available and those being researched and developed. Before examining these in detail, it is worth looking at the context in which such decisions are made. It is one characterised above all by unpredictability.

This chapter describes the kind of situation in the field which farmers and pest management agents face in practice. They have to locate the pests, assess the potential danger to crops and decide, in the light of available resources, what action to take. While the ultimate objective in both grasshopper and locust control is crop protection, the pests require different strategies.

Locusts

During periods of recession, the Desert Locust leads the life of a true nomad, surviving in its Saharan desert environment by migrating between temporary areas of greenery which spring up in response to sporadic and patchy falls of rain. On the rare occasions when rainfall is abundant and frequent, the locust can multiply rapidly and gregarise, forming the bands and swarms which are a potential precursor of plague.

Control strategy is therefore to keep track of such developments, and in the light of the information gathered, to decide on the most cost-effective treatment to prevent populations building up to dangerous levels. A wrong decision can result in unnecessary expenditure and pesticide use, which has environmental costs as well; equally it can aggravate the situation, and lead to invasion of cropland by swarms of hungry locusts. Moreover, the size and inaccessibility of the areas involved in the monitoring process means it is a specialised task, since ideally it involves the use of satellite technology in conjunction with the other surveying methods described in the preceding chapter.

Decisions often have to be taken on the basis of inadequate information

While there are FAO guidelines to assist with such evaluation, it requires requires considerable expertise and experience. And in reality, decisions often have to be taken on the basis of inadequate information.

Desert Locust control is further complicated by the need for regional cooperation. The Sahelian croplands are far removed from the locusts' summer breeding areas in the desert plains of Mali, Niger, Mauritania and Chad: the "frontline" states responsible for monitoring population build-up. Any escaping swarms tend first to move north and northwest to invade the Maghreb countries. Only following spring breeding in the these northern areas will the new generations sweep south and threaten Sahelian crops (see maps on pp6-7). This is what happened in 1988, and in previous plagues. In recognition of this, Moroccan and Algerian locust control units actively assist the Sahelian plant protection services.

Once a plague has developed, the focus has to switch to crop protection. The Sahel is too vast and invading swarms too mobile for control operations to have a realistic chance of bringing a plague to an end, or even substantially reducing the numbers of insects. The best strategy is to concentrate on minimising damage. At this point, tactics are similar to those in grasshopper control, reflecting the need for risk reduction rather than risk avoidance. At this point, too, farmers and

Gregarious hopper bands of the Desert Locust in Mali during the 1986-88 plague.

George Popov

George Popov

village brigades have a part to play, as they do throughout grasshopper control strategy. They can monitor and report swarm movements, and actively protect their crops against any locally hatching locusts.

A millet field in Mauritania after locusts have stripped it of the leaves. Even though the grain remains, the harvest will be badly affected.

Grasshoppers

Grasshopper control is rather different to that of the Desert Locust and is closer to the day-to-day work of the Sahelian farmer. Little attention is paid to grasshopper infestations outside cropland, unless they clearly represent a potential threat to farmers. Since cultivated areas represent a fraction of the total area of the Sahel, a strategy which focuses on crop protection, rather than preventing build-up of grasshopper populations throughout the region, minimises the use of pesticides and helps to maintain a balanced ecosystem, in which grasshoppers are a link in the food chain.

The sense of such a policy was reinforced by the fact that the massive spraying campaigns of 1986 did little to reduce grasshopper infestations of crops in the following years. Damage to pastureland is generally tolerable, given the established nomadic practice of moving from one area of grazing to another, although sometimes local infestations are so severe that they completely disrupt grazing patterns.

The fictional but realistic situations described in the rest of this chapter focus mainly on the activities of the Senegalese Grasshopper, but farming communities may find themselves dealing with one or more of about 20 different species. The control decisions which face farmers and field staff have a seasonal aspect, and vary according to whether they are dealing with locally hatching grasshopper nymphs, or adults migrating from elsewhere.

Early season
With the arrival of the first rains, millet germinates incredibly fast. Even after only one significant wetting, the process is under way. The natural vegetation also responds very quickly, and so do the insects. Just 20 mm of rainfall is thought to trigger grasshopper hatching, for example. The young immature insects, the "hoppers", do not initially move far from where they hatch, but they are voracious eaters and often the nearest or the only green plants are the young millet shoots.

A millet field contains relatively few, widely spaced plants: in a very short time an entire field can be destroyed. The only witness to this is the farmer, who may try to prevent the hoppers from damaging his young millet by physically stopping them from entering the field, or by using a chemical dust barrier or some other chemical treatment. Where this is impossible or the losses are discovered too late, the only option is to start sowing again, if the farmer has seed and labour available.

Resowing increases the uncertainty and the likelihood of crop failure. A farmer may end up with as much as he or she would have done from the original sowing, but the new plants will have missed some of the season's early rains and it may be too late for them to complete their cycle and produce grain.

The biggest danger from hoppers comes from those that gregarise and move about in marching bands, the earthbound equivalent of swarms. Simpler methods that might prevent single insects or small numbers from entering fields are unlikely to deter large numbers of marching bands. However, if a village brigade has been formed, trained and equipped, marching bands present an easy target.

If a pest control officer discovers large numbers of grasshoppers early in the season he or she has a number of options. Where village brigades have been formed, and the necessary equipment and pesticides are available, it may be

Jeremy Hartley/Panos Pictures

possible to carry out a treatment—but only if the insects are already in or near fields and are perceived by farmers as a threat. Since 1986, this village brigade approach has been increasingly promoted throughout the Sahel, especially in Senegal, Mali, Niger and Burkina Faso.

Spraying against grasshoppers in Burkina Faso. The patchiness of the growing plants indicates how precarious are the prospects of good yields under any circumstances in the Sahel.

Where the officer is working more or less alone, but has the necessary equipment and chemicals, he or she has to assess whether the threat is sufficient for time and resources to be used on one concentration of insects, given that there might be more serious infestations elsewhere in the area. The problem is that the agent cannot know whether further stocks are likely to be made available during the season. Moreover, the agent has to take account of the fact that, especially later in the season, other pests such as birds, head-feeding beetles and caterpillars enter the picture.

A decision against treatment, on the basis that insects are not very numerous or will probably soon move away, can be difficult to sustain if local farmers are in favour of treatment or if village chiefs or local government officials exert pressure. No national service agent is immune from this. Pest control agents have been known to display sacks full of grasshopper or locust cadavers after treatment to counteract local criticism. Decisions as to whether or not to treat are particularly difficult

Agents are always operating in situations of enormous uncertainty

when pastureland is infested or threatened, as there is no immediate threat to crops.

Ultimately, the decision to treat should be part of local strategy, which should reflect regional strategy. This requires regular and rapid communication within and between organisations. Otherwise, the officer is left trying to interpret local conditions and national strategy on his or her own, or having to rely on information received too late to locate and treat the hopper outbreaks. In such circumstances, they will tend to make decisions that incur the least risk to his or her job, to the local farmers and to the environment, in that order.

Mid-season

As the season goes on, in addition to the grasshoppers that hatched locally, adults may fly in from elsewhere. Both sets of insects will reproduce. The millet has grown and is more able to withstand a certain amount of damage but the possibility of replacing lost plants is reduced since the time for any new sowings to reach maturity is becoming short.

Flying swarms of locusts and large concentrations of grasshoppers present the biggest threat, and generate an even more difficult set of decisions. In 1988, for example, crop protection staff in Dilly, northwestern Mali, found large populations of Senegalese Grasshoppers near crops. Pesticides were used on several occasions on groups which came too close to village margins. Larger populations were known to be further away but it was felt that resources should not be wasted on them, especially since it was likely that once the insects could fly they would go north, probably into uninhabited areas of Mali or Mauritania. The outlying insects did, in fact, fly north—but just before leaving, they flew into local fields and in two or three days caused enormous damage. A great deal of rapid spraying from a vehicle was carried out but once flying swarms settle in a crop, major losses are unavoidable. It would be extremely harsh to judge this a failure to predict the situation accurately. No matter how much experience agents have, they are always operating in situations of enormous uncertainty.

Late season

Towards the end of the season the chances of harvesting anything from resowing become negligible. Farmers are left to harvest what they can from their existing plants. Anxiety mounts when it does not rain for a few days, and turns to a dull hopelessness if the drought runs to 10 or 12 days. If the rain does fall, the relief is tangible. The millet produces heads which flower and then form soft grains, which are extremely vulnerable to attack.

End-of-season attacks by flying swarms are likely to be the most destructive and irrevocable, partly because of vulnerability of the crop but also because, if control has been impossible or ineffective, the swarms are far more numerous than in early or mid-season. The surrounding natural vegetation is drying out and the crops are the only really green plants available. Locusts and grasshoppers may feed on the leaves, which is unlikely to affect the harvest, but more probably will attack the grain. The migration pattern of the Senegalese Grasshopper is closely linked to the movement of the rains. They tend to move north in early summer and then southwards again in September, which can mean they reach certain croplands just at the point when the grain is ready for harvest.

Control operations at this stage can absorb a massive proportion of campaign resources, partly because of the importance of trying to prevent such potentially devastating losses. If, earlier on, people have taken decisions not to treat, more resources are left for late-season work—when there may seem little point in trying to conserve chemicals. However,

Yaya Coulibaly of Dali village, Mali, surveys his millet after grasshoppers have attacked it. His chances of harvesting anything from the remains are next to nothing.

Mike Goldwater/Network

A decision against treatment can be hard to sustain
although it is now even more important to limit damage, it is very much more difficult to do so. Political pressure to show evidence of activity can also be very powerful at this time. Many end-of-season treatments seem to be carried out after the harvest is safely over.

Aerial spraying is almost always required because of the scale of the problem and the necessity to act fast, and also because ground control against highly mobile flying adults in tall full-grown crops is difficult and largely ineffective. Spraying can usually only be carried out in the early morning, before it becomes so hot that the pesticide vaporises and is carried aloft by updrafts before reaching the ground. When a large number of swarms are invading, it is not possible to respond to all the calls for help. By this stage, protecting crops has become a massive task that cannot be pre-planned and depends on rapid responses to incomplete information. In such circumstances, serious crop losses are inevitable.

During the 1986-90 grasshopper control campaigns, the bulk of pesticide use occurred in late season. Experience has shown, however, that treatment of adult grasshopper populations after harvest is not useful and will not significantly reduce the population size of subsequent generations. By avoiding post-harvest pesticide application, the consumption of pesticides and unnecessary environmental pollution can be greatly reduced.

CHAPTER 6

Control methods

Traditional methods of locust and grasshopper control, some of which are described in Chapter Two, have been used for centuries. Apart from the destruction of egg masses, trench digging and burning, other methods of control involve releasing poultry, which feed on locusts and grasshoppers, into fields of crops, and using cattle to eat off and trample the grass in locust-breeding areas. Changing the timing of planting, using more resistant varieties and intercropping are other strategies to reduce damage. However, when natural conditions are in the pests' favour, their populations grow at a rate which overwhelms such efforts.

The following is an overview of most other types of method of control available, in terms of the resources they require and the results they yield [1]. Given that chemicals are currently the most widespread method for dealing with major outbreaks of locusts and grasshoppers, this chapter begins with an examination of the issues surrounding their use.

The Pesticide Debate

It has been argued that probably the greatest cost to the Sahelian environment from locust plagues stems not from the insects but from human activities, notably the use and misuse of synthetic chemical pesticides. Criticism of pesticides is widespread and there is a growing body of opinion in industrialised countries totally against their use. Some even contend that it would be preferable for locust plagues to run their course, whatever the scale of damage. This suggestion is examined in Chapter Eight. In spite of undoubted problems, pesticides will probably be the most important means available for some time to come to protect Sahelian farmers.

The effects of pesticides on an ecosystem depend on a variety of factors, making accurate predictions difficult. Ideally, a pesticide comes into contact with the target pests, kills them and then disappears. This is rarely the case. Usually

Pesticide treatments may actually contribute to the problem
pesticides are toxic to a range of organisms, regardless of their pest status. There are, for example, no chemical pesticides that are specific to grasshoppers or locusts. Indeed, it may be that the natural enemies of grasshoppers and locusts are more susceptible to the pesticides than the target pests. If this is the case, then pesticide treatments may actually contribute to the problem.

When pesticides do not achieve the anticipated level of success, treatments are often repeated at ever increasing levels of frequency and strength. Yet the reason for the apparent failure may well be that the poison is killing not only the target pest but also its natural enemies [2]. Lukas Brader, former director of plant production and protection at the Food and Agriculture Organization (FAO), has suggested that something like this may be behind the extraordinary outbreaks of grasshoppers in the Sahel in 1989 [3]. His theory was that control operations after 1985 may have killed so many of the grasshoppers' natural enemies that for the first time they were able to reproduce unchecked. However, because the ecology of most of the species concerned, and of Sahelian systems in general, are as yet insufficiently understood, this remains no more than speculation.

A longer-term difficulty of pesticide use is that they can be concentrated in the food chain. One of the first and most dramatic cases of this was at Clear Lake in California in the 1950s. Minute quantities of DDT, sprayed into the environment to kill midges, were found concentrated 10,000 times in the carcasses of Western Grebes [4]. Organo-chlorides, the products most likely to destroy organisms which they are not intended to kill, have now been largely withdrawn from use where such a possibility is likely.

Yet the use of the organo-chloride dieldrin in locust control continued until 1987. Indeed, the efficiency of pesticides for locust control, and their effects on the environment, have only relatively recently begun to be systematically investigated. In other areas of pest control, especially in arable farming, problems of resistance, environmental damage and other costs have been carefully examined and a range of more appropriate techniques proposed and tested.

The fact that so little is known about the Sahelian environment increases current fears about damage. Pesticides can be assumed to be killing many of its invertebrate fauna,

USAID

such as bees, wasps, beetles, butterflies and moths, but without regular observation and monitoring there can be no real prediction of the effects. It is evident, however, that Sahelian ecosystems are more "fragile" and easily thrown off balance than most tropical or temperate systems and that they take longer to recover their equilibrium.

Spraying pesticide onto locust hoppers. The environmental cost of large-scale spraying campaigns have not been fully researched but there is growing disquiet at the probable damage to Sahelian plant and animal life.

By far the most extensive work on the environmental impacts of grasshopper and locust control pesticides is the Locustox project in Senegal. Begun in 1991, Locustox is coordinated by FAO and funded mainly by the Dutch government [5]. Work on the potential for biological control, funded by the Dutch, French, Norwegian, German, UK and US governments, is now under way (see pp67-71).

Progress on environmental impact has been hampered by the need to start from rudimentaries: collecting basic information on non-target organisms. Similarly, work on biological control had to begin with detailed surveys of the natural enemies and pathogens—organisms or substances that cause disease—of locusts and grasshoppers.

In 1990, FAO began producing and periodically updating a register of research and development projects on the Desert Locust [6]. This includes short descriptions of recent, current and proposed work on different aspects of pest biology and control. This useful publication should facilitate collaboration

Some characteristics of pesticides

Until the Second World War people used to kill insects with naturally occurring products which were either simple chemicals, such as arsenic, or derived from plants. Chemicals have been used to kill insects for only about one hundred years. In the Sahel, locusts and grasshoppers were controlled by mechanical means only—using trenches and barriers, ploughing up egg-pods and so on—until the 1940s, when poison baits were gradually introduced. The baits were usually bran laced with some sort of arsenic compound.

During the 1940s, the chemical industries of Europe began to produce toxic substances that could be used to kill insect pests, firstly organo-chlorides, followed by organo-phosphorus compounds and carbamates. Although natural pyrethrum had been known about for a long time, it was only much later that pyrethroids were synthesised for use as chemical pesticides. These remain the main groups of insecticides used today.

The most important characteristics of pesticides are their toxicity: how much is required to kill a pest, and their persistence: how long they remain toxic. There are considerable problems in assessing both of these qualities.

The toxicity of a pesticide depends not only on how active the chemical is but also on how it gets into the animal, the nature and condition of the animal, and physical conditions such as temperature and humidity. The measure used to compare the toxicity of pesticides is the LD50, which is the quantity (in milligrams per kilogram or parts per million: ppm) required to kill 50% of a batch of test animals, usually laboratory rats. The differences between oral and dermal LD50s (whether taken by mouth or through the skin) give an indication of the way toxicity is affected by variable conditions. The toxicity of the pure pesticide is not as important as the toxicity of the formulation in which it is used.

The persistence of a pesticide is also dependent on a range of factors. These include its formulation, for example, dust, granule or liquid; the environment in which it is deposited, for example, air, plants, soil or cement walls; and again conditions such as temperature and humidity. Despite this uncertainty it is possible to rank pesticides as more or less dangerous. The World Health Organization uses a system to classify pesticides which is universally accepted. The table below is for liquid pesticides. As more and more ultra-low volume (ULV) hand-held sprays are made available, which require the use of liquid concentrates, the risk of poisoning is greatly heightened. As the table opposite shows, dusts are usually 2-5% in concentration, whereas the active ingredient in liquid pesticides is far higher.

WHO class	Oral LD50	Dermal LD50	Amount of pesticide to kill an average person
Ia extremely hazardous	20	40	A taste to a teaspoon
Ib highly hazardous	20-200	40-400	
II moderately hazardous	200-2000	400-4000	A teaspoon to a tablespoon
III slightly hazardous	>2000	>4000	A tablespoon to several cupsful

between researchers and the identification of areas where more work is needed. What is striking is that much of the work is at quite a basic stage, even though the Desert Locust is better studied than most grasshopper and other locust pests.

Given the importance of locusts as a pest, such a low level of basic information may seem extraordinary, but it is the price of research cuts since the mid-1960s, imposed when control seemed simple and pesticides were acceptable. Professor Chapman, well known for his work on locusts and grasshoppers, described the cost of keeping research teams in the outbreak areas as "increasingly prohibitive", not least because of the lack of infrastructure to support their work [7]. Yet such cost-cutting can be a false economy. Once an ecosystem has been badly affected, it can take far more time and expense to work out the causes and repair the damage than to avoid it in the first place.

Dieldrin
Evidence of environmental damage caused by the persistent organo-chloride pesticides such as dieldrin, BHC, aldrin and

Pesticides	Oral LD50	Dermal LD50	WHO class	Form used	Amount (g/ha)
Organo-chlorides					
BHC	88	900	II	2-5% dust	400
				20% liquid	300
Dieldrin	46	60	Ia	20% liquid	10-35
Carbamates					
Carbaryl	850	2000	II	48% liquid	1000
Propoxur	100	800	II	25% liquid	125
Organo-phosphorus					
Diazinon	75	450	II	60-100% ULV*	500
Fenitrothion	250	3000	II	50% ULV	500
Malathion	2800	4100	III	96% ULV	1000
Pyrethroids					
Cypermethrin	4000		III		36
A-cypermethrin			III		10
Lambda-cyhalothrin	79	632	II	0.8% ULV	15

* ultra-low volume (spray)

USAID

A village store, where sacks of pesticides are kept alongside bags of grain and animal feed, with potentially lethal results. DDT, has been so overwhelming that most European and North American states have banned them, with a few exceptions for special circumstances. Donors involved in grasshopper and locust control programmes will not provide these products and in some cases have refused to support campaigns which use them. Dieldrin was produced by the Royal Dutch Shell group until 1990, which has now dismantled its plant and since 1991 has stopped selling dieldrin for any purpose.

There is thus no longer any debate over the use of dieldrin, but the way in which the decision to discontinue was taken remains a sensitive issue. Donors, with USAID (the US government aid agency) taking the lead, simply stated that they would not supply it or support activities connected with its use. In 1988, FAO convened a meeting on the issue, at which evidence for and against its use was presented. There was no dispute over the efficacy of dieldrin for killing locusts. Indeed, because of the unpredictability of locust plagues and the difficulty of gaining precise information, dieldrin—by virtue of its persistence and toxicity—was particularly well-suited to the job. The primary function of persistent insecticides is the laying of barriers that kill insects which pass across them, because all that is required is information that high numbers exist in the area. Less persistent chemicals cannot be used in this way, since they become inactive within days.

However, based on the weight of the evidence at the FAO meeting on the potential environmental impact of the pesticide—it had been banned for use in most industrialised countries from as early as 1974—donors took a strong stand against the use of dieldrin in the 1986-90 campaign.

The ban on dieldrin was imposed by donors

Those who query this decision-making process point out that there was no recently acquired reliable data on its efficiency, or on its long-term environmental effects, in the locust-affected countries. In effect, the ban on dieldrin was imposed on these countries by donor organisations, which based their decision on research in more temperate zones—evidence which they judged in the circumstances to be sufficient. There was no wide consultation of control organisations, individual extension workers or Sahelian farmers. Some argue that the different, arid conditions of the Sahel would have broken dieldrin down to a less environmentally harmful product [8], although the problem of its persistence in the food chain would have remained.

However, the result was that the ban prevailed—and in the view of one specialist this was a case when "enlightened pressure was used to bring about an eclectic if sometimes reluctant consensus among the donor agencies and recipient countries [9]."

Apart from the barrier strip method described, persistent chemicals are also effective for spraying during periods of invasion because the area remains toxic to successive invasions, whereas less persistent chemicals require repeated spraying. Supporters of dieldrin maintain that this practice could be as damaging to the environment as a single treatment of dieldrin. No comparative tests have been made to prove this either way.

There is, however, some evidence from trials in Senegal (the Locustox project) that the "safer" less persistent pesticides in current use are fairly toxic in the shorter term to many non-target organisms. These include practically all aquatic animals, many birds and insects—among them some of the natural enemies of locusts. The fledglings of insect-eating birds are particularly affected because of being deprived of their food source. Such findings underline the care needed in the use of even allegedly safe pesticides.

Obsolete or unusable pesticides have become a hazard

The difficulty with all the arguments about dieldin and pesticides use is the lack of systematic supporting evidence. During the 1970s, locust control methods involving dieldrin were never really put to the test and no data were collected on their efficiency. It was simply economic to spray barriers of dieldrin once each season. Since there were no major plagues during this time, a possible conclusion is that the methods were successful and that the 1988 plague resulted from their absence. While it is true that the quality of survey and control operations was poor, it seems more logical to recognise the major role played by the weather. The rains leading up to the 1988 plague differed so much from those in the preceding decade that they allowed a plague to develop at a time when virtually none of the requirements for successful control were fulfilled.

What the dieldrin debate highlights is the need for much wider debate, within the North and the South, about the merits and disadvantages of pesticide use, and for more research into the effectiveness of chemical treatments. There appears to be little correlation between one year's control operations in specific areas and the following year's outbreaks. A site which has been heavily treated one year often ends up being just as densely infested the next. The locusts' rapidity of movement and their tendency to re-invade are additional complicating factors, and the lack of concrete information means that people with a vested interest can praise or criticise treatment strategy without contradiction. All too often the assumption is simply that the larger the area treated, the more successful the campaign.

Storage and disposal

Although dieldrin was banned from use in the 1986-90 campaign, stocks had been piling up throughout the Sahel since the 1960s. The older containers had deteriorated and by 1990 the problem of unwanted or increasingly unusable pesticides, not just dieldrin, had become a recognised hazard. USAID funded a conference in Niamey, Niger in 1990 for the sole purpose of discussing the problems involved in disposal of old and surplus stocks of pesticides [10].

Problems have arisen from excessive or inappropriately timed donations, improper storage, and badly packaged and labelled stocks. Large quantities are sometimes divided up and sold in makeshift containers, such as old liquor bottles or grain sacks. Discarded, leaking drums can poison humans and animals and pollute water supplies. And the empty containers are a valuable commodity: farmers often use them for storing water, grain and animal feed. They are also recycled into use as walls or roofs or flow regulators for irrigation. But however well rinsed, no container can be completely free of pesticide.

In June 1991, through a collaboration between USAID, the government of Niger, Shell, the German technical assistance agency (GTZ) and several other Dutch agencies, some 54,000 litres of dieldrin and 20,000 litres of solvent were successfully transferred, by truck and ship, from Niger to Holland for incineration. But current estimates suggest that at least 20 million and up to 60 million litres of unwanted hazardous chemicals are still in need of disposal in 30 African countries.

The hazardous waste of war

The risk of poisoning and pollution from surplus stocks of pesticide originally intended for locust and grasshopper control is a recognised problem in the Sahel. But the war in Somalia turned the threat into reality. Quantities of pesticides had been assembled by DLCO-EA at Hargeisa, now the capital of Somaliland (formerly the northern part of Somalia). The city had been a strategic point from which to prevent the formation of locust swarms in the Red Sea coastal areas and protect fertile areas further inland.

But DLCO-EA operations in Somalia ceased during the civil war and the compound had become a victim of the fighting—badly damaged, abandoned and looted, it had become a shelter for homeless families. Containers had been smashed, broken into, and their chemical contents spilled far and wide. At least 20,000 litres had leaked out, saturating the soil. Torn or missing labels meant it was impossible to identify the chemicals, which included dieldrin and smaller quatities of DDT.

The danger arose not only from direct contact with the exposed chemicals. The compound is situated in a depression in which rainwater gathers before feeding into the main river which runs through the middle of the city. Hargeisa's Chinese-built water system has been destroyed by the war. Although some repairs are being carried out, most of the city's residents have been forced to take scarce drinking water from the chemically polluted river.

Government and DLCO-EA officials recognised the dangers both to the city's population and to those further downstream and to human and animal life on the Gulf of Aden coastline. Attempts were made to cover the spilled chemicals with sand, using bulldozers. But the government had too few resources to do so with any great success. They contacted the International Register of Potentially Toxic Chemicals in Geneva, which has provided advice on how to identify the chemicals and mitigate the effects of the spillage.

Abdi Yusuf Duale, Somaliland

Control Methods Using Pesticides

Ground treatment

While other methods can be carried out by professional locust control staff without local participation, pesticide treatment on foot usually requires the involvement of farmers.

The simplest of these methods involves using dusting bags. Farmers can be quickly trained in their use and often make their own equipment. If insects are clearly threatening fields, farmers are often prepared to work with pest control staff directly. Where high densities of hoppers are known to be nearby, farmers can usually be persuaded to help there, or at least to treat the edges of their fields. The pesticides used are dilute dusts, which are relatively safe but bulky to transport, necessitating delivery to villages during the dry season.

Another method, widely promoted in the Sahel, is the use of ULV (ultra-low volume) hand-held sprayers, such as MicronUlva. While lightweight and efficient when properly handled, these use a much more concentrated product and need constant re-filling, so there is increased risk of human poisoning from leakage, careless use or inadequate training or protection. They also need a constant supply of batteries, which can be another constraint on their use.

The key feature of treatments on foot is the relatively small area covered. Moreover, this kind of control obviously depends on good cooperation between pest control staff and farmers, with professional staff providing training and supervision and ensuring that the necessary materials are delivered in time, and farmers helping to detect infestations and provide labour for their control. Such cooperation is rare but not unknown; both sides have to see that they have something to gain from it. Good management training is essential.

The creation of farmer-level or village brigades to carry out early season control has made considerable progress over the last seven years and it is generally agreed that the policy should be pursued, not least because it is consistent with the move towards decentralisation of services. While their main use has been to apply pesticides, especially against the season's first generation of grasshoppers, some of the many hundreds of brigades formed throughout the Sahel have become involved in egg-pod collection and destruction. This works especially well with species which lay in dense groups, such as *Kraussaria angulifera, Cataloipus cymbiferus* and

Hieroglyphus daganensis.

It is vital for individual farmers and those in brigades to receive proper training and continued support, and in particular, advice on protecting themselves from pesticides. One advantage of keeping control in the hands of trained and experienced staff is the lower risk of accidents. There are too many reports of pesticide poisoning for any complacency about the dangers [11]. In many areas of the Sahel, inadequate medical services and low levels of individual health may also mean that illness from pesticide poisoning sometimes goes unrecognised.

As well as the increasing concern about the dangers posed

USAID *Crop Protection* clip art book

by chemicals to humans and to the environment, there is also a reluctance to create a dependency within brigades on donations of pesticides and spray equipment, with all the problems of recurrent costs that such a policy implies. Thus donors are anxious to promote the brigades' services for monitoring and early warning, and to encourage the use of non-chemical control methods, such as egg-pod collection, and to build on traditional practices and knowledge (see Integrated Pest Management, p70). Weeding and clearing the margins of fields could be another brigade activity which helps to reduce grasshopper attacks on crops.

Agricultural extension materials illustrate the right and the wrong way to prepare pesticides for use.

Treatment by vehicle

Spraying by vehicle rather than on foot covers a larger area but requires more resources. It is the responsibility of the crop protection services, and farmers have had little role to play. Exhaust nozzle sprayers, which have been used on vehicles for many years, have sometimes been criticised for spraying inefficiently and putting strain on vehicle engines. Newer, more efficient spray machines, such as the Ulvamast, that do not rely on the vehicle engine for power, are becoming

Village brigades in Niger

Subsistence agriculture occupies 85-90% of the population of Niger and is based on growing millet, groundnuts and *niebe* (cowpeas) on sandy soils, sorghum in the valleys, and rice on irrigated land. Yields are very low and it is estimated that pests destroy 20%-30% of the annual crop: almost 230,000 tonnes in all, and equivalent to the country's annual food deficit. Pest control is therefore a vital element of Niger's strategy for food self-reliance.

In 1970, a centralised office for plant protection was set up with technical and financial assistance from other countries. It is reinforced by plant protection posts situated at the main border entries to Niger. One of the office's main functions is the promotion of self-reliance in plant protection, based on the conviction that farmer participation is essential to rural development.

Village brigades have played a valuable role in fighting crop pests. Each year they treat an average of 120,000 hectares, a figure which could increase with a better supply of equipment. To help follow-up, a map indicating where brigades have been trained has been distributed to all trained farmers.

One member of each brigade is trained in basic emergency procedures and routine maintenance of the equipment supplied (motorised equipment worn on the back, portable and pressurised sprayers). In each district there is a repair workshop supervised by a mechanic, and brigades are also provided with repair equipment.

Mamadou Issoufou, a farmer in Goudel, 7 km from Niamey, is a member of a locust control brigade. In his opinion, the brigades are a positive development: "In the past, only the managers, and the district and area heads, put the sprayers on their backs and went out to treat the fields. The farmers were mere spectators. When the office for plant protection acknowledged the need for farmer participation, and organised a widespread information campaign to recruit farmers, I decided to volunteer."

The brigades are able to treat very small fields where it would not be cost-effective to use aerial spraying. According to Mr Issoufou, they have prevented infestations in record time. In 1988, a year of unusually severe locust attacks, state mobilisation of all the country's brigades ensured that locusts were fought in the worst-affected areas.

Brigades are organised by the village council, which selects five farmers to help with pest control on behalf of the village in affected areas. The criteria for membership are—besides being an active farmer—providing services voluntarily, attending training sessions and project days, being between 18 and 45 years of age and "having a community spirit". Mamadou Issoufou believes brigades could be made more effective if the owner of each field treated paid brigade members "a little something—just enough to buy a bar of soap".

"Brigades will continue to be effective as long as they are well treated; they should not be mobilised without receiving anything in exchange. After all, we are members of the same community and we do not have time to tend our own fields. We need something to leave our families during our absence. We also need cards showing we are a member of a brigade, allowing us to buy products and equipment in other districts."

Not everyone is prepared to volunteer to join a brigade. Koda Abdoulay, a farmer in

Saga-Hondo, 23 km from Niamey, is typical of many younger men who leave the village during the non-cropping season, from October to March.

"I leave with a few friends of my own age for the Côte d'Ivoire. The old farmers know we never stay in the village once the main agricultural season is over. Another reason [why people are reluctant to join brigades] is that pesticides kill the people who use them. In a neighbouring village, one brigade member lost two of his children who had been playing with a tin of pesticide, and even the nurse could do nothing about it. You see, in the past we had no protective equipment."

But Koda Abdoulay is grateful that the brigades exist. He remembers the bad grasshopper and locust attacks of 1984 and 1988, "when the insects left us nothing worth talking about in our fields." Traditional methods—trapping the larvae in trenches and burning the fully-grown insects—proved insufficient. "On our family plot of 5 hectares, we only harvested 17 bundles [approximately 300 kg] of millet and 13 bundles of sorghum. In a normal year, without any major locust invasion, we harvest over 150 bundles of millet and 80 bundles of sorghum.

"In 1989, thank God, the plant protection office set up brigades in our region. Our village has five farmers who have been specially trained. In the event of an invasion, we will call on them to get rid of the locusts. Of course, we will not just fold our arms and watch them work. The trench system can still be used, and we will help them. Recently, our village development council built a store to house the pest control equipment donated by the state, as well as a large number of pesticide products. If our brigade runs out of products, we have the use of several carts which can fetch supplies from elsewhere in the district."

Despite his praise for the brigades, Koda Abdoulay believes that locust control is more effective with the use of planes. "We have seen this in the case of our fields. It is really very effective. The locusts are destroyed in no time. It's much better than the Land Rovers which the plant protection officers use. They simply trample our crops and don't even treat the whole area, whereas planes are very good at spraying.

"It must be said that some members of the brigade are very slow. Before they take any action, they first come and go to our fields to take locust samples 'for identification purposes', as they say, and only afterwards do they try to fight them. But during this time the locusts continue to nibble away at our crops. It really is time wasted."

Ibrahim Cheik Diop, Niger

available. But to test and refine this kind of equipment needs collaboration between fieldworkers, trainers, scientists, technicians, manufacturers and donors—something not easily achieved.

Aerial treatment

Aerial spraying becomes necessary when the scale of infestation is too enormous for ground operations. In addition to the provision of ground support, fuel and pesticides, and the maintenance of landing strips, there is the problem of identifying target areas and monitoring the effectiveness of

George Popov

A village brigade in the Banamba region of Mali with their haul of grasshopper egg-pods.

treatment. This requires scrupulous coordination and an understanding by both ground and air teams of the constraints under which they operate. Training, and above all experience, are vital to success. Paradoxically, while aerial intervention can be far more rapid than any other form of treatment, it can also be held up for long periods because of the initial logistical problems.

Aerial treatment is dangerous work and the drop-out rate among pilots is dramatic. All aerial treatment is now in the form of ULV spray (0.5-1 litre per hectare), and considerable expertise and experience are required to ensure correct functioning as well as the right dose for the pesticide in use. If a campaign is to be successful, treatments must also be accurately assessed for their efficiency: that is, for the percentage of insects killed. These difficult tasks are further complicated when new and different kinds of pesticide are introduced. The skill of the ground team is important, as they have to survey dense populations, indicate targets, guide pilots and check on treatment accuracy and effectiveness. The only possible short-cut in this kind of work involves the use of helicopters, which allow scouts to combine spraying and ground surveys.

As the comment of Nigerien farmer Koda Abdoulay suggests (see p65), the speed and scale of aerial spraying can be impressive, but there is a need to rethink dependency on aircraft for control operations. In 1988 and 1989 much more aerial spraying took place than was probably necessary, largely because the aircraft and pesticides were available. Moreover, even aerial spraying can be ineffective and wasteful, especially in the case of grasshoppers, unless it is well-timed and precisely targeted on the most vulnerable fields before harvest—conditions which are difficult to meet in the Sahel. *Aerial spraying can be ineffective and wasteful*

Biological Methods

Biological control using a pest's natural enemies has been successful in a number of situations. The main advantages of such techniques is that they are usually specific to the pests concerned, and safe for operators. There are few of the environmental concerns that surround pesticide use. In addition, where biological control has been successful, the economic benefits tend to be greater than the costs of researching and carrying out the control method—costs which can sometimes be considerably lower than those required to develop and produce a new synthetic chemical insecticide. Biological control has worked well in environments such as orchards, forests, and glass-houses, where the pest and its enemy can be in constant association and where conditions remain relatively constant.

Biological control depends on the pest's enemy, usually a parasite or a predator, keeping the pest at such low levels that it does no economic damage. If pest numbers begin to increase, the enemy also multiplies and so reduces the pest population again. Applying such a tactic to locusts, which are endemic over large areas, presents obvious difficulties, as does their patchy distribution and rapid movement over long distances, because their enemies would not move so easily from one area to another. There are, however, isolated success stories: the first recorded introduction of a predator, the Indian Mynah bird *(Acridotheres tristis)* from India to Mauritius in 1762 did substantially reduce the Red Locust problem.

Biological pesticides

Work has been carried out on the protozoan, *Nosema locustae*, which has shown some promise in controlling grasshoppers, but results in general have been disappointing and unpredictable. The organism does not kill the insects immediately but makes them less active and reduces fecundity.

Using fungi to fight locusts

An internationally-funded attempt to find a non-chemical antidote to locusts is showing its first promising results. After testing about 100 strains of fungi—including new ones from the field as well as some from established collections—a team of scientists coordinated by the International Institute of Biological Control in England has settled on a strain of the fungus *Metarhizium*.

Mixed with oil which sticks to the insects, *Metarhizium* has emerged as "the perfect locust disease": host-specific and harmless to vertebrates and animals. No side-effects or environmental damage have been detected, says the head of the research team, Dr Chris Prior. If confirmed by subsequent field tests, its safety would represent an important advance on chemical treatments, which fail to discriminate between insects and so kill potentially useful varieties as well as locusts.

As chemical pesticides came under increasing fire, the industrialised countries that contribute half the cost of locust control commissioned the Institute to find a biological alternative. The Institute is a non-profit organisation with 29 member countries, and the 10 researchers come from Benin, Niger, The Netherlands and Britain.

Metarhizium and the related fungus *Beauveria* (focus of an associated USAID-funded research programme), were well-known to the scientists because related strains had been used in combating the Colorado potato beetle, frog-hoppers in Brazil and maize stem-borers in China, among other pests.

"We had to show that the fungi could be mixed with the right sort of oil and would be stable and remain infective in the relevant temperature and humidity," says Prior. "We have proved that this is possible." In addition, the fungi can be sprayed with equipment already in use and can be grown on materials available in countries likely to be affected by locusts.

"They are cheap and easy to produce in bulk," says Prior. "They grow on simple things like rice, cereal grain and brewery waste. So far these fungi are the only locust diseases proven to be able to invade the insects through their bodies. Most others have to be swallowed to be effective."

Adults were killed in five days in laboratory tests, and in seven days in field tests in Benin and Niger. To destroy a swarm may require just one application of the ULV (ultra-low volume) spray. Farmers accustomed to seeing immediate results from chemical pesticides might find five to seven days a long time, but Prior considers it a minor disadvantage compared with the overall benefits.

He admits that introducing a new technique is not a straightforward matter: "The concept of spraying a living fungus is an alien idea. People must be persuaded to change their pesticide and go for something different." Although there is a great deal of environmental awareness in Africa, he adds, people working in the field still need to recognise the damaging effects of chemical pesticides. But he also points out that though "locusts don't often do major economic damage, when they do, it is so disastrous that no country will willingly face the risk of locusts arriving."

The hope is that if biological pesticides can be developed locally, afflicted countries will no longer need to rely on foreign assistance. Conventional delivery systems can be used for spraying, eliminating the need for specially designed equipment. Dr Prior, however, does not envisage commercial use of the formulations of fungal spores until at least 1996, even though "we are satisfied that the new approach is feasible. We hope to interest the donors to fund the project further. We need to do more field tests on the different species of grasshoppers."

Field tests were carried out in 1992 in Benin and Niger, and in Madagascar in collaboration with the German technical aid agency (GTZ), which is working on a crop protection programme in the country.

Prasanna Probyn

This might provide worthwhile control in some circumstances. Rigorous trials would require the study of whole populations of insects over a period of time, clearly a difficult task when the target species is very mobile and when field study— identifying the enemies and assessing their effect—is only possible for a few months each year.

Research is being carried out on the possibilities of using fungi to kill locusts. As with pesticidal control, it will involve direct spraying on to pest populations, as the spores of the fungi infect the insects after contact. The effectiveness of these organisms is usually much greater in humid environments and their effectiveness in the Sahel is currently being tested (see box opposite). Research into other fungi, such as *Beauveria bassiana*, is under way for grasshopper control. Studies and field trials in Mali and Cape Verde began in 1990 and were initially disappointing. Results in 1991 were more successful and suggest early problems have been overcome. A 1992 report stated that: "Mortality levels compare favourably with those achieved with chemical pesticides, without any environmental and public health risks [12]."

Most other pathogens—organisms which cause disease— need to be eaten by the insects as bait and are therefore less practical as control agents. Again, the advantage over chemical pesticides would be improved environmental and operator safety, although since fungi take several days to kill the insects, pesticides may still be required to prevent damage when pests are near to crops. The use of bacteria and viruses might also have potential for locust control in the future. The work in this area began by searching for, developing and testing more virulent strains of the disease-causing organisms, which would be more effective in control [13].

Other Methods

Some other possible methods of control require long-term research and development. One is the use of insect growth regulators (IGRs), that disrupt the normal development of locusts so that they fail to reproduce. Such products have been developed against other insect pests and have the advantages of being very specific and relatively safe [14].

IGRs are believed to have potential as replacements for dieldrin in barrier strip treatments and have recently been shown to provide useful levels of control of grasshoppers and locusts in field trials in Mali, Senegal, Madagascar and elsewhere. These are important first steps, but there are many more to be taken before commercial quantities are available and operators adequately trained: their effectiveness depends greatly on being applied at the correct stage in the life cycle. The environmental effects also need to be carefully assessed because they may affect other organisms.

Putting locusts and grasshoppers off their food is another biologically based method now being investigated. The insects can be deterred from attacking plants that have been sprayed with particular plant extracts. One such "anti-feedant" is neem oil, currently under trial in Niger. CARE (an international NGO), GTZ (the German government technical aid agency), CIDA (the Canadian government aid agency) and USAID are all funding research projects. Neem is also believed to have potential as a pesticide: once sprayed, swarms land on the ground and seem disinclined to resume flight.

Another control approach, which has also proved successful with other pests, involves pheromones, the chemicals that insects produce to signal to each other and thus control their behaviour (see opposite). An attractive objective would be the prevention or disruption of gregarisation. However, while this might seem a worthwhile goal, most experienced locust experts consider that a non-swarming locust which might still migrate would be a more difficult pest problem than a swarming one, in exactly the same way that grasshoppers are more difficult to control effectively than locusts.

Integrated Pest Management

Integrated pest management (IPM) is the coordinated use of multiple tactics to assure stable crop production and to keep pest damage below an acceptable level. Acceptable is usually

Tricking locusts into staying single

A team of scientists in Kenya is trying to fight the threat from locusts by identifying and then tampering with the causes of various stages of locust behaviour.

At the heart of the research is one of the major mysteries of locust life: what causes the essentially harmless solitary locust to combine with millions of others in voracious swarms that can cover more than 1,000 sq km, flying over 300 km a day? Says Professor Thomas Odhiambo, director of the Nairobi-based International Centre of Insect Physiology and Ecology (ICIPE): "The aim is to keep the locusts firmly on the ground."

The search for new ways of controlling locusts stems from concerns about the environmental and human damage caused by toxic synthetic pesticides, such as Malathion, currently in use. ICIPE scientists are working on the hypothesis that locust behaviour is controlled by natural chemicals in their bodies, which could be isolated, synthesised and used against them.

A major effort is underway to de-code the insect's chemical language, particularly the signals that trigger the formation of swarms, synchronised and accelerated sexual maturity, and communal egg-laying. A swarm multiplies 30-fold every time breeding occurs, which in ideal conditions can be three or four times a year. Locusts manage to find their mates even though they may be up to 10 metres apart, suggesting the existence of pheromones (substances secreted by an animal for detection and response by another of the same species).

Professor El Sayed El Bashir, who heads the Institute's locust control programme, says it is also possible that certain plants contain signal chemicals which may also influence the behaviour of locusts. "Some aspects of this research have been studied before," he says, "but the tools were rudimentary and funding was limited." Finance for ICIPE's research is provided by a range of bilateral and international organisations, and has paid for a locust-rearing facility at its Duduville ("Insect town") headquarters a few kilometres from Nairobi.

The scientists have also been watching locusts in the insect's natural habitat on Sudan's Red Sea coast. In addition, they are investigating the possibility of biological control of the pests. The problem is that few pathogens survive the harsh conditions in areas of locust infestation.

As Bashir stresses, many other scientists are working on locust control programmes: "It is a regional pest which knows no boundaries."

Dorothy Munyakho, founder member, Interlink Rural Information Service, Nairobi, Kenya

defined in economic terms and in some cases it has been possible to establish "economic injury thresholds": the point at which it becomes cheaper to use a control measure than allow further pest damage. More recently, the concept of reducing environmental hazards and restoring ecological equilibrium has been added to the original philosophy of IPM.

IPM has had significant effects on thinking about pest control. By focusing attention on its end purpose it has helped to validate cultural control measures, such as planting different varieties or intercropping, and to reduce the use of chemical pesticides. This was especially important when pest control was heavily dependent on pesticides and damage limitation measures were being devalued or ignored.

As far as locusts and grasshoppers are concerned, it is difficult to disagree with the basic ideas of IPM. Even though chemicals are currently the most obvious methods of controlling them, few would argue for the exclusion of all other methods. Biological methods may never be sufficient on their own but could form a valuable part of a comprehensive package of measures. Other relevant IPM strategies include developing small industries to produce locust meal for food or neem extract as an anti-feedant, sound land management including reforestation, and generally more emphasis on preparedness and prevention rather than emergency control measures.

Accepting the principles behind IPM encourages a more thorough, wide-ranging approach to pest control. Taken to extremes, in the case of grasshoppers and locusts it means that resolving political conflicts or reducing national debts can be thought of as part of tackling the constraints on improving control measures. More practically, it endorses the idea that one should not rule out any particular method because it will not bring about control on its own. A number of apparently

How to transport pesticides and avoid contaminating food and grain or poisoning livestock.

USAID *Crop Protection* clip art book

small-scale practices might make useful contributions to the overall effort to reduce losses.

The philosophy of IPM is also useful in focusing attention on the overall aim of control campaigns. Chapter Eight looks in more detail at the way that campaigns have been funded and run and the different sets of priorities involved.

IPM of grasshoppers is currently more feasible than it is of locusts

IPM of grasshoppers, especially the non-migratory majority, is currently more feasible than it is of locusts. A five-year Grasshopper IPM Project in the United States is researching ways to control grasshoppers with the minimum environmental impact. But some of the methods that have become possible in the control of other insect pests do not easily apply to grasshoppers or locusts. For example, cultural control measures—those relating to the ways crops are grown—are not easily integrated with the practices used by resource-poor farmers whose main preoccupation is with scarce and unpredictable rainfall. Nevertheless, some simple measures, such as regular weeding and clearing the edges of fields, have proved effective against grasshopper infestations.

Another problem with IPM for locust control is the idea of economic injury levels or thresholds, which are much more easily defined for pests that do not migrate. Where studies have successfully defined a critical density of pests, farmers can survey the crop and, if they find more pests than that critical density, know that it is worth their while to commence treatment. For this process to be viable it is necessary to be able to calculate the cost of the treatment, the value of the crop and, most difficult of all, the probable evolution of pest numbers in the crop and consequent damage. All these are extremely difficult where locust attacks are concerned.

Attempts have been made to describe critical densities of locusts and grasshoppers. The guidelines produced by USAID in a 1987 Strategy Paper [15] are different from those in the USAID *Locust/Grasshopper Management Operations Guidebook* [16], while PRIFAS has produced a third set of thresholds on its "Cube Expert" [17]. All three tables have qualifying remarks referring to, for example, the different stages of the insects' life-cycle, whether they are gregarious or solitary, the time of the year, the state of the natural vegetation and so on. This just shows how difficult it is to produce guidelines applicable to all situations. And given the difficulties of estimating the value of losses from locust attack

No method
is likely to
be successful
on its own

(see Chapter Two, pp17-19), it is clearly particularly hard to make informed decisions about how much money should be spent on trying to prevent them.

A further difficulty with introducing IPM to locust campaigns is that ideally it requires flexible, informed decision-making mechanisms so that the most appropriate package of control measures for any particular time and place can be quickly chosen and implemented. Not only is the range of methods against locusts currently somewhat limited, but attempts to react with speed and flexibility are fraught with difficulty. Problems include the many different levels of decision-makers, inaccessible terrain and the obstacles to rapid communication in the Sahel, and the large number of variables involved in the way a plague develops.

What this underlines, however, is the importance of investigating a wide range of ways to improve grasshopper and locust control. As this chapter has already made clear, no single method is likely to be successful on its own but a combination might provide the necessary level of control at an economically and environmentally acceptable price. And even when major upsurges are under way and emergency measures being adopted, elements of IPM are still relevant, such as making the optimum use of all resources, rather than the maximum use of one such as aerial spraying, and consistently minimising the hazards to people and the environment from chemical treatments.

CHAPTER 7

Institutional aspects of control

A range of institutions are involved with grasshopper and locust control; better mutual understanding of each other's roles and priorities would facilitate coordination and collaboration—the keys to successful management of a regional problem.

Changes in the roles of the regional organisations mean that the burden of field work has now passed to the staff of the national services of the member states, and that regional coordination and information sharing has been divided between a number of institutions. Before examining how this relatively new situation is developing, it is important to review the history of the regional organisations.

Regional Organisations

In the 1950s, some of the locust and grasshopper control responsibilities of the colonial period were shifted to the UN's Food and Agriculture Organization (FAO), which was also to coordinate the activities of the different organisations and donors involved. National crop protection agencies and regional organisations replaced the colonial structures as the African states gained independence. One such organisation (OICMA) ceased operations in 1986 and today there are three semi-autonomous regional organisations (see box overleaf).

In addition, there are three FAO Regional Commissions which deal with migratory pests that transcend national boundaries: in Northwest Africa, the Near East and Southwest Asia. In these areas control is handled primarily by the national crop protection agencies, but the Commissions coordinate surveys, control, training and research. The fact that a number of countries in the Arabian Peninsula, Iran, Pakistan, India, as well as the North African countries have their own locust control organisations is a reflection of the enormous area affected by the insects.

Since the mid-1980s and the general shift of responsibilities

Regional locust control organisations

OICMA—Organisation Internationale pour la lutte contre le Criquet Migrateur Africain (International Organisation against the African Migratory Locust).
Headquarters: Bamako, Mali. Member states: Burkina Faso, Cameroon, Central African Republic, Chad, Congo, The Gambia, Côte d'Ivoire, Mali, Mauritania, Niger, Nigeria, Senegal, Sierra Leone, Togo, Uganda, Zaire.
Set up in 1948 by France, Belgium and the UK, who had cooperated on locust control since the 1920s, OICMA was responsible for control of the African Migratory Locust, *Locusta migratoria migratorioides.* Following independence, it was taken over by the emergent African states which comprised the region most affected by plagues of this species. OICMA was officially closed in 1986 due to lack of financial support by its member states, but the fact that there has been no major outbreak of the African Migratory Locust for nearly 50 years has obviously been a factor in its demise.

OCLALAV—Organisation Commune de Lutte Anti-Acridienne et de Lutte Anti-Aviaire (Joint Locust and Bird Control Organisation).
Headquarters: Dakar, Senegal. Member states: Mauritania, Senegal, Mali, Niger, Chad, Burkina Faso, Benin, Côte d'Ivoire, Cameroon, The Gambia.
Set up in 1965, OCLALAV was initially responsible for the control of the Desert Locust and bird pests. Through inadequate funding it has not been fully operational for some years and since 1989 the responsibility for control has been placed on the "front line" states: Mali, Mauritania, Chad and Niger. Currently OCLALAV is responsible for coordinating training and research.

DLCO-EA—Desert Locust Control Organization for Eastern Africa.
Member states: Djibouti, Ethiopia, Kenya, Somalia, Sudan, Tanzania, Uganda. Established 1962. DLCO-EA is responsible for supporting national plant protection services in the area and coordinating control operations. It overlaps with national services and some confusion exists over its role with non-locust pests. (There was an agreement in 1976 to undertake control of bird pests, armyworms and tsetse flies when locusts are not a major problem.)

IRLCO-CSA—International Red Locust Control Organisation for Central and Southern Africa.
Member states: Kenya, Uganda, Tanzania, Zambia, Malawi, Zimbabwe, Botswana, Swaziland, Mozambique.
This organisation also suffers from a lack of member states' payments but the situation is improving.

from regional to national level—a move aided and abetted by donors—the role of regional organisations has been continuing to evolve. Ironically, it has been easier to evaluate the work of these organisations by their absence than by their activity. During the 1986-88 plague, it was clear that the absence of effective regional coordination made control more difficult. And in 1985, when funds from the emergency campaign for control of the Senegalese Grasshopper were made available to the now defunct OICMA, it rapidly mounted control operations in Mali—suggesting that lack of finance, rather than something more fundamental, had prevented it from functioning.

OCLALAV had similar funding problems but the member states did not recommend closure. Instead, in 1987, an attempt was made to streamline the operation, by passing the management of control operations to the four West African "frontline states" most affected by the Desert Locust. This was followed by a rescue attempt in 1989, when it was proposed that OCLALAV pass the practical work of monitoring and control to national services and simply maintain an overall coordination role. Yet it could only fulfil such a role if it had the confidence of its members—the same members who had been failing to pay their dues.

The regional organisations were in this sense allowed to weaken fatally by the member states. Yet the donors were presented with a dilemma. Obviously they could not insist on the participation of individual countries, but there did seem to be possibilities for renegotiating regional structures that were not pursued. A number of attempts were made to modify or merge the regional organisations but without success. Donors withdrew support in an uncoordinated manner and a reduction in the mandate of the regional organisations became inevitable given the parallel lack of commitment of member states. Yet the decision to support national programmes seems to have been made without sufficient recognition of the implications for regional coordination.

Some have argued that the regional locust control organisations were formed during the colonial period and could never have been appropriate to post-independence Africa. Colonial structures had the authority to override national interests or autonomy, whereas a regional organisation of independent states had no such authority and therefore had to be better suited to a coordinating than an executive role.

But regional organisations possessed certain advantages for working within and between states, advantages which have become clearer as the national services have struggled to take on some of their functions. Employees of national services are subject to certain pressures, not least political. For example, field staff are sometimes asked to provide protection for their own villages, or for the home villages of influential people.

Confidence was lost in the regional organisations The national director may be asked a whole range of favours which may be legitimate in the cultural context but do not make for efficient management. Individual states must be able to demonstrate to their neighbours that they are fulfilling their roles; inactivity in one country may cause pest damage in another. Furthermore, the different states are effectively competing for resources from the donors. It is not surprising that those responsible for national services sometimes over-state the dangers faced by their country and the successes of their control operations.

Using state apparatus makes coordination between countries more cumbersome than using the regional organisation's structures. Information exchange within the Sahel for control operations, and with the outside world to mobilise aid, has been difficult. In the past, regional organisations disseminated information in two directions: to their field staff to carry out their work; and to the region, the donors and UN organisations. FAO now has this second role at the international level, while the new-style OCLALAV transmits information within West Africa. Yet FAO's attempt to coordinate data is constrained by its dependence on national organisations to provide it. And national services are not obliged to feed information to FAO, except perhaps when hopeful of receiving aid from donors.

There are, therefore, several stages at which data are interpreted and, since the dissemination from FAO is predominantly to donor organisations and representatives, there is considerable delay before the information returns to the field from Rome. And because the FAO bulletins do not contain the raw data, they can be hard to interpret.

Few would promote the view that the old regional organisations were perfect—they clearly were not. Regional organisations have problems throughout the world, even where resources are plentiful and there are closer cultural ties and vested interests, as in certain European federations and affiliations. Ultimately, their effectiveness was diminished not because of lack of technical ability but because confidence was lost in their usefulness, management and financial status. Underfunding then led to inefficiency and reduced morale, further undermining the member states' commitment. And given the enormous pressures on individual countries' budgets, it was hard to continue payments—especially to organisations designed to prevent something which is only seen as a threat at times of plague.

This last point is, of course, a major difficulty, and is one reason why the scaling down of the regional organisations may not be in itself a bad thing. Indeed, the ideal way for such institutions to operate would be to maintain a core structure and then have the ability to scale operations up and down according to need. But this kind of flexibility is difficult to create and is particularly difficult to sustain when job security, understandably, is a major issue.

Today, OICMA is closed, DLCO is much reduced but still operational, OCLALAV still has some functions, while IRLCO is relatively strong and well supported. Whatever one's view of the changes in their role and status, the important thing is to analyse any problems these have created for national services, and to explore ways of resolving them, without losing sight of other options such as different kinds of regional initiative.

One example of such an initiative is the attempt to develop the Regional Preventive Control Plan for the Desert Locust in western and northwestern Africa. The plan's fate remains undecided but the process of debating and developing the options, with an emphasis on prevention, brought together representatives of the International Fund for Agriculture and Development (IFAD), FAO and the affected nations. Discussions highlighted the importance of flexibility in such a plan, for example being able to target grasshoppers when necessary, and the need to build up the resources of affected countries so that in the long term they can carry out such work with less input from donors.

Another example, this time of regional coordination, is the way that the Centre for Application of Agrometeorology and Hydrology for the Sahel (AGRHYMET) has assumed responsibility for including in its regional bulletins a summary of the current situation with regard to pest outbreaks and the relative risk posed to crops. As an organisation already oriented to crop protection, it could be seen as a lead organisation to expand this role, combining as it does related information on the weather, plants and pests.

National Services

The national crop protection services are now the main organisations responsible for grasshopper and locust control in most countries, because of their mandate to protect crops.

George Popov

Certain grasshopper species lay their eggs under trees and shrubs. Agents need regular training as new control methods are developed and knowledge increases about the different species.

They take over when infestations become too large-scale for individual farmers to control. Usually part of the Ministry of Agriculture, these services may combine in control efforts with other agencies, such as forestry departments, research institutes, weather bureaux, transport services and sometimes even the military—for example, pilots may assist with aerial spraying.

But the Sahelian states are among the poorest in the world, both in terms of traditional measures of wealth such as GNP per capita or more sensitive measures such as the UNDP Human Development Index. National budgets throughout the region are under immense strain. Public services are often inadequate, sometimes non-existent. Not surprisingly, agricultural extension and plant protection services suffer immense constraints.

Someone reading the useful USAID *Locust/Grasshopper Management Operations Guidebook* [1] might be left with the impression that extension agents are in daily contact with farmers, that they have intimate knowledge of habitats in their areas and that their educational backgrounds enable them to be easily trained in a range of new techniques relevant to pest control. While this might be true of some situations, it is, as the book suggests, more often an ideal to aim for. In practice,

many extension agents have had only a weak theoretical rather *National*
than practical education. Their local knowledge may be slim *services are*
and since they often have no means of transport, their ability to *chronically*
increase that knowledge and to make regular contact with *underfunded*
farmers is severely limited. A report to FAO by Paul Teng in
1985 examined the strengths of plant protection services in 15
West and Central African states [2]. It looked at 17 areas of
work, including training, research, current levels of knowledge
and equipment. In nine of these categories not one country had
"good" provision, only "moderate" or "poor".

Similar shortcomings can be expected at the level of
management and coordination. Relatively well-funded public
services in industrialised countries do not escape these
problems and it is only reasonable to expect difficulties where
such services are chronically underfunded. Lack of resources
and personnel clearly affects the ability of national plant
protection services to carry out routine duties and to scale up
their operations with external funding during emergencies.

However, some of the shortcomings identified by Teng
reflect the fact that many pest management services were set
up in the mid-1980s, when the regional institutions were
scaling down and when emergency operations against
grasshoppers and locusts were getting under way. This dictated
the nature of their operations for the next four or five years.
Since 1990, there have been deliberate attempts to broaden the
scope of their work from short-term emergency measures to
cover the full spectrum of pest management and to strengthen
their research and extension capacities.

Training and support
In some cases the staff of the old regional organisations are
now part of the national services. Re-deployed OICMA and
OCLALAV staff, for example, brought much experience to
their own national crop protection services, but many are
nearing retirement. There is a great need for the training and
retraining of pest control staff, not least because of continual
developments in understanding of the biology of the pests and
in potential control measures. It is now necessary to be
familiar with a much wider range of grasshopper species, as
well as with the many different pesticides and spray
mechanisms available.

The crucial importance of radio communication has already
been mentioned. Agents need to be able to maintain and

Agents in the field are the key to successful control operate high frequency transceiver radios and know the rudiments of vehicle maintenance. Operators at headquarters must be able to rely on agents sending regular, concise radio reports which utilise the information collected in the field, and can then be evaluated and responded to.

An improvement in relations between pest control staff and farmers is called for, as these have not been universally good. Farmers have sometimes been suspicious of government officers, who have in turn tended to be less than respectful to farmers.

These problems are surmountable, but only if they are acknowledged. Government staff often have a difficult time in remote rural areas, especially if they are not provided with the required resources. Support visits from senior staff may be infrequent and opportunities for extra training or refresher courses rarer still. It is not surprising that agents fail to win the respect of local people if they are perceived as being unable to fulfil their role. Irregular salary payments compound the problems. Moreover, the practice of providing generous donor-subsidised *per diem* payments for travel tends to encourage a management style with little delegation; a series of field trips can effectively double the annual salary of a pest management official.

Any anti-locust organisation has to face the difficult task of maintaining staff morale. The long periods with no perceived threat of locust attack undermine the authority of pest control staff. Yet one successful treatment of insect pests can repair the damage of years of apparent inactivity. Given the problems just listed, it is unsurprisingly difficult to recruit skilled personnel willing to stay in isolated posts for long periods. Where there is a shortage of qualified people, as is the case in most Sahelian states, most would prefer a post in a large town to a difficult job up-country. It may be easier to find local people who can be trained to the level required.

Agents in the field are the key to successful control of major insect pests—but only if they are integrated both with the local farmers and into the national and regional networks. Staff of the old regional organisations felt that they were valued members of an important international network and prided themselves on doing a job well. This spirit has yet to be built up in most government services but it can be created. Linking practical pest control work with agricultural research activities

A training manual shows the way to apply pesticides using a dusting bag: with face protected and the wind blowing the chemicals away.

in outlying areas and with broader rural development organisations could provide more interest and incentive.

Education and training is important at village level, too. INSAH (Institut du Sahel) is using a set of innovative training manuals on Integrated Pest Management in five local languages to promote literacy training. By encouraging the development of writing and numeracy skills through a relevant and practical subject, the project also promotes the farmers' confidence in tackling crop pests using a range of options, rather than just depending on pesticides.

Bilateral and Multilateral Donors

Donor agencies play a key role in locust and grasshopper control. Enormous sums of money were devoted to campaigns during the last plague period (see table overleaf). Over the period 1986-89 a total of US$192 million was made available by bilateral donors and US$60.5 million by multilateral donors. Not all of this was destined for the Sahel: the figures include aid to East, Southern and North Africa and to some Asian countries.

Much of this aid, especially in the earlier years, was from disaster funds. Some, however, was in the form of project aid, and incorporated longer-term objectives. There is no doubt that

Donor assistance to locust and grasshopper control programmes, 1986-89 (US dollars) [4]

Donors	1986	1987[a]	1988	1989 (Jan-May)	Total
Bilateral donors	31,931,292	27,587,167	81,739,094	50,803,000	192,060,553
Multilateral donors	16,503,461	2,744,104	32,223,880	9,073,730	60,545,175
Non-government organisations	1,211,460	133,000[b]	1,111,000	0	2,455,460
TOTAL	**49,646,213**	**30,464,271**[a] **+20,000,000**[c] **50,464,271**	**115,073,974**	**59,876,730**	**255,061,188** **+20,000,000**[c] **275,061,188**

a Includes only assistance to Sahelian and West African countries.
b Includes only assistance from ActionAid to Gambia.
c An additional $20 million was given by donors for programmes in northwest African countries,
   Sudan, Ethiopia, and Yemen.

Source: Adapted from *A Plague of Locusts—Special Report*, US Congress, 1990

donor governments are sensitive to calls for emergency aid and that huge sums of money can be mobilised at such times. It is also clear that the control operations during the last emergency could not have been mounted without the aid of these major donors and that further assistance will be required for some time to come.

A lot of the money was spent on pesticides, flying hours and spray equipment: the perceived needs of the emergency operations. Many of the bilateral donors were constrained by internal rules to provide domestically produced goods wherever possible: the principle of tied aid. These donors also have their own specific decision-making systems, with varying amounts of authority vested in their field and home offices, which works against efficient coordination of their efforts.

FAO is the most important of the multilateral agencies, partly because of the sums of money involved but more because of its coordinating role. It works at several levels: it assists coordination of the regional organisations, sponsors the three Regional Commissions and supports donor coordination meetings within each country where there is an emergency campaign. It is these meetings that should go some way to improving the situation. However, their main purpose is as a forum for the sharing of information which, although crucial in itself, does not ensure coordination.

During the recent 1986-88 emergency campaign, FAO distributed aid from the international donor community, including the United Nations Development Programme (UNDP), through the Emergency Centre for Locust Operation (ECLO) based at FAO in Rome. ELCO was closed in 1990, but reactivated in late 1992, in response to the developing Desert Locust upsurge in the Red Sea coastal areas.

Non-Government Organisations

In recent years non-government organisations (NGOs) in the field of aid and development have grown enormously in both number and importance. They represent a potential additional force in grasshopper and locust control.

In the first place, they can act as donors. This is not normally the case, because most NGOs do not see themselves as performing or subsidising government services—although how much they already fulfil this role in other areas such as health, education and agricultural extension is debatable. It is also argued that the sums required for a control campaign are well beyond the normal expenditure of most NGOs.

However, Oxfam contributed £10,000 to the 1988 campaign in Mali, a small amount in overall terms but one which earned generous plaudits from George Popov, an FAO consultant then in Mali [3]. Oxfam gave the money to ensure that areas where they had projects were surveyed, thus protecting groups that they were already supporting. For the national plant protection service the money was important because it was made available at a time when other donors were still reticent.

In most Sahelian states there are NGO-coordinating bodies who might be able to increase the importance of individual NGO donations by combining a number of smaller sums, and monitoring their expenditure. The role of coordinating bodies is complicated by the fact that NGOs vary a great deal in size, sources of funding, declared aims, modes of operation, available skills and management. Yet since the actual control work is being managed by the national service, coordination between NGOs, and between them and the state, is essential. In Senegal, the NGOs formed a separate body to integrate their locust control activities, CIONGLA (Inter-NGO Department of Acridian Control), although if the existing coordinating body is working well this should hardly be necessary.

NGO staff often spend more time in villages and have better

At first sight this might seem like a healthy shrub, but the branches are covered with locusts, not leaves.

George Popov

contact with farmers than those in the state services do. Where this is the case, they can fulfil another role, by helping with the exchange of information between farmers and government, and in the organisation of communal activities. This has already happened in the formation of some village brigades.

One drawback is that most NGOs operate within limited geographical areas. The national service has therefore to collaborate with a number of NGOs if it is to cover significant ground. In addition, NGOs often see their interventions as being confined to one sector of activity: staff on a well-digging programme, for example, may not feel that they should be involved in pest control. The decision should perhaps be made by the local population, who could indicate whether they would like NGO staff to help or act as go-betweens.

NGO staff often have better contact with farmers than those in state services

Another critical factor is the attitude of the managers of the national services: where they see the usefulness of collaboration, progress can be made. Clearly, there is a great deal of work to be done here, most of which will fall to the coordinating bodies. They should explore with their membership what they can do to help, and with the government service what is required.

In the box overleaf on CIONGLA, Senegalese farmers express a desire to take a more active role in plant protection. They also reveal to Senegalese journalist Hibrahima Bakhoum their feeling that as soon as the Desert Locust was no longer a threat, the money dried up. Some donors question why control-oriented funds should flow in the absence of compelling need. But the general perception of many Sahelian farmers, voiced in Bakhoum's article, needs to be recognised: that once a locust outbreak has died down, funding is withdrawn and little provision is made for training people or maintaining equipment and research, in order to build up expertise and alternative methods of prevention and control.

Conflict and Cooperation

Coordination and cooperation between institutions in the region become even more difficult when there is conflict between or within countries. The situation in the Sahel has become worse as competition over a deteriorating resource base has fed into existing political and ethnic tensions. Areas of conflict in the Sahel during the 1980s and 1990s included: Western Sahara (involving Morocco, Mauritania and the Polisario); the border between Mauritania and Senegal; the border between Mali and Mauritania; the border between Mali and Burkina Faso; northern Mali; Chad, in the north, where there was both internal fighting and war with the Libyan army, and in certain areas bordering Sudan; Sudan; and Ethiopia (where there was fighting between government and Eritrean and Tigrayan forces). In some of these areas conflict was short-lived, and in certain cases need not have prevented efficient monitoring or control of locusts.

"Without the farmers' initiative, there will be no salvation"

"We must start afresh, go back to square one. We will not succeed unless the instinct for plant protection is integrated into the general process of agricultural production."

This is the verdict of Abdoul Aziz Sy, coordinator of Senegal's Inter-NGO Department of Acridian Control (CIONGLA). Since 1985, Senegal has adopted a new approach towards plant protection and locust control which, although based on sound principles, has had only limited success because, in Mr Sy's view, some fundamental errors of judgement have been made.

In the past, farmers were in charge of production only, in the restrictive sense of the word, leaving the state to see to crop protection. The advent in 1985 of a new agricultural policy, based on the "progressive disengagement" of the state and "responsibilisation" of farmers, coincided precisely with the return of the rains and the awakening of grasshoppers and other crop enemies.

Aware of the extent of the threat posed by the pests, NGOs active in the rural areas met with the Minister for Rural Development in June 1986 and offered their support in the locust control campaign. The meeting led to the formation of CIONGLA which soon had around 50 members.

Swift action was required. The objective was training and information on locust detection and control techniques. The country is divided into eight intervention zones, each placed under the responsibility of one NGO which coordinates the actions of the other partners. Trained representatives from these in turn convey their knowledge to some 900 "farmer-leaders". Transmitting information in this way was a key innovation.

The idea is said to have originated in Kolda, in Casamance, south Senegal, a region where dynamic agricultural organisations already existed. The plant protection departments had been able to collaborate with these in the fight against parasitic insects.

When CIONGLA decided to adopt this framework, they made their first mistake: the structures which were set up do not correspond to the farmers' concerns, especially to the way they "choose" their leaders. Long years of one-party rule in Senegal bequeathed undemocratic structures which have survived more recent constitutional reforms. The traditional system always gave priority to people influential with the authorities. Popularity was not important. Economics, and allegiance to the local *marabout* (religious leader/decision-maker), were much more important factors.

The NGOs, who wanted to make farmers aware of their rights and responsibilities on the basis of universal suffrage, have often found their work blocked. Furthermore, the goods handed to the farmer-leaders have not always reached their intended goal, as political or "religious" factors have influenced distribution. The alternative solution of distributing supplies on the basis of a quota per farmer has also turned out to be ineffective since the distribution of locusts is not correspondingly even. Some farmers who did not see many locusts were landed with stocks of pesticides, whereas supplies were lacking in places where infestations exceeded bearable limits.

Cooperation with farmers is essential. The Senegalese farmer, Mr Sy points out, knows what he wants. He is as quick to listen to the technicians as to "bury" them, along with their projects. "As soon as the farmer realises that you want to lumber him with a programme he does not fancy, he digs a hole and lets you come forward, his arms wide open. What he has just set up is meant for you."

New approaches

In 1988, the year of the Desert Locust, the technicians, authorities and farmer organisations were all caught unawares. The following year they were on the alert for an "explosive situation". But this turned out to be a false alarm. The Desert Locust "had gone back to the sands of the Sahara". With its disappearance, money became scarce and in 1990 the main means of control—aircraft—were sent back to base.

Meanwhile, the migratory Senegalese Grasshopper was coming to the fore and causing terrible damage. Louga region is said to have lost almost 20% of its millet and *niebe* to grasshoppers in 1989.

In Tatene, Ousmane Ngom, chairperson of the village action committee organised by CIONGLA, is adamant: "It is the grasshoppers that are our biggest problem." They are also harder to control than the gregarious Desert Locusts. According to Mr Ngom, in 1989 Tatene lost an important part of its *niebe*, "almost all the cultivated millet", and an appreciable part of its groundnut crop. However, local farmers said they felt "encouraged" by the support given by the "Thiès technicians" and found the training session, funded by CIONGLA, useful.

Training has become CIONGLA's favourite theme. This is because, according to its coordinator, "it is unrealistic" to think that the state will be able to carry on the responsibility for treatment: from now on the farmer will have to integrate crop protection into crop production. In the Thiès region alone, CIONGLA and the regional plant protection organisation carried out 115 successful training sessions for 232 village action committees during the 1990 campaign.

As far as means are concerned, some hope is in sight. An NGO is to initiate an equipment programme for the village committees. Each village will only have to make a contribution. Unfortunately, in Tatene, as in many other places, the money coffers are empty.

Other containers are full to the brim: those used by Tatene inhabitants to collect the egg-pods which they have started to dig up in anticipation of the imminent rains. In one day, those rallied by the committee for a "mine clearance" operation removed 35 kilos—a future generation of 600,000 grasshoppers.

"The fire is inside the house. We cannot lounge around waiting for the firemen to arrive," one farmer remarked. His pragmatism is characteristic of the new philosophy amongst farmers in the Senegalese rural environment.

Hibrahima Bakhoum, Senegal

Instances of cooperation between affected countries include the sending of experienced agents to assist other national teams or providing surveillance near border regions of neighbouring countries. Morocco has given such assistance to Niger and Mauritania, as has Algeria to Niger and Mali. Under normal circumstances, the plant protection services of Mali and Mauritania cooperate along their border area, within which large populations of the Senegalese Grasshopper

A village meeting, Senegal. Farmer brigades are playing an increasing role in crop protection as well as production.

Jeremy Hartley/Panos Pictures

migrate. The Malian service has sent staff on joint survey missions with Mauritanian staff and has treated crops in Mauritania, not least because at the end of the season the grasshoppers move south to cause damage in Mali. In 1988, tension in the area was sufficient to prevent this kind of collaboration.

The conflict between Senegal and Mauritania has also affected control operations. Many of the most important farming areas and breeding grounds of ˈlocusts and grasshoppers, where the Mauritanian plant protection service normally concentrates its activities, lie along the Senegal river. Any escalation of hostilities at a critical time for survey or treatment of locust populations clearly has severe consequences.

Chad, like most Sahelian countries, contains huge areas of suitable breeding ground for the Desert Locust which are too large to be covered by ground surveys. In 1987 and 1988 the continuing conflict with Libya meant that aerial surveying in the north was forbidden. Limited aerial surveys in 1988 coupled with some ground surveys and some good guesswork indicated that breeding did, in fact, take place and did substantially contribute to the plague. In October 1990, poor relations between Chad and Sudan prevented the surveying of large areas on both sides of their common border.

During the control operations in Western Sahara in 1988, a DC7 spray plane was shot down by Polisario, and in 1990 a French pilot was killed (on the ground) in Niger while on a research mission. In Ethiopia, one spray plane was shot down and another shot at in 1987. In spite of much diplomatic activity during that year to find ways of carrying out aerial treatments of parts of Eritrea and Tigray, it was not possible for these operations to be carried out from Ethiopia. Plans were made to fly from within Sudan, and permission sought from the Ethiopian government by FAO and DCLO-EA, on the basis of the practical threat posed by the breeding populations to Ethiopia and neighbouring states.

Other donors were reluctant to apply pressure to the Ethiopian government since this might be seen to prejudice their position with respect to the political situation. Clearly a regional organisation is best placed to conduct such negotiations, since it approaches the matter on a purely technical basis, but even here politics often hamper and at times halt control operations. Even the non-partisan FAO knows such constraints. In 1988-89, Saudi Arabia initially resisted FAO efforts to send experts to the peninsula to assess Desert Locust populations there.

Observers disagree about the relative significance of the breeding grounds in the different areas of conflict. The earlier breeding in the Horn, the breeding in northeast Chad in mid-1987 and that in the Western Sahara in late 1987 and early 1988 all contributed to the build-up of the 1988 plague. But the effects of the failure to survey and treat in the conflict areas can never be fully evaluated because of the region's lucky escape from a potentially prolonged sequence of plague years.

The different conflicts in the Sahel may also influence control operations adversely in more subtle ways—affecting, for example, the allocation of resources. Donors may reasonably decide that aid to an area of conflict is less likely to be cost-efficient and so divert resources to areas which are in less need. In Sudan in 1990 all donors greatly reduced their activities. In 1991, the German government's technical aid agency, GTZ, aborted plans to locate a ground surveillance team in Mali due to conflict in Northern Mali and pulled out of Niger in 1992 for similar reasons.

CHAPTER 8

Looking ahead

66 It is a sad reflection on our society that we shall probably
have to wait for another series of massive locust plagues
before politicians and financiers will take a serious long-term
look at the problem [1]," wrote Professor Chapman, a
renowned expert on locust control, in the 1970s. The truth of
his words was borne out in the 1980s. Lack of preparedness,
the low priority given to research and training in the past,
inadequate data collection, poor coordination, and missed
opportunities in the early stages of plague build-up all
contributed to millions of dollars being spent on emergency
rather than long-term measures.

Today, however, there are signs that the different agencies
involved are beginning to do much more to maintain continuity
of support during a period of recession. A resurgence of
interest in pest management and growing concern for the
Sahelian environment has highlighted the past neglect of
practical research on the major species and on the need to
develop alternative methods of prevention and control.

There is a recognition that there has been too much reliance
on expensive emergency crop protection tactics, the aim of
which is to destroy locusts near croplands during plagues, and
that more resources should be directed to strategic control,
whereby plagues would be halted or prevented by monitoring
Desert Locust populations in the breeding areas and using a
range of pest management methods to control them [2].

Control of locusts and grasshoppers also needs to be looked
at in the wider development context, for the constraints are
much more than technical and include policy, institutional,
social and economic factors. There has been a tendency to
tackle pest management in isolation and not relate it to wider,
more long-term development issues. Land tenure and access to
credit, for example, are factors which clearly affect farmers'
capacity to invest in long-term preventive measures.

This chapter looks at the possibilities for reform and the

"The link between famine and locusts is questionable" benefits that better control will bring. Many of the problems associated with the complex task of grasshopper and locust control, while more widely recognised and debated, remain. National plant protection services are still struggling to cope with migrant insect pests. Pest management strategies still suffer from conflicting assumptions, priorities and assessments of the situation. Unless real progress is made to improve preparedness, when the next plague builds up—and the locusts will be back—Chapman's words may yet again prove uncomfortably close to the truth.

Assumptions

One of the issues discussed in the preceding chapters is the wide range of actors involved in grasshopper and locust control and the difficulties of coordination. These different actors do not always share objectives and priorities. Perhaps one of the first questions to be asked is, since so much money has been poured in to emergency campaigns, what is the generally accepted purpose of control?

A tacit and widely held assumption about grasshopper and locust control is that the objective is to avoid widespread famine. This assumes that the damage done is always on a grand scale and significantly threatens food security. Yet, concludes one report: "The link between famine or food shortages and locusts and grasshoppers is questionable....Damage [in the recent plague] was less than drought would produce [3]."

It is, however, extremely difficult to establish the exact relationship between locust attack and famine because of the paucity and poor quality of agricultural production data. Moreover, national statistics do not take into consideration the localised nature of losses and the social as well as economic effects on individual families or communities, whether farmers or herders. Descriptions of overall food losses disguise the fact that many people are threatened not just by food shortages but by having their means of production totally destroyed. Plagues do cause hardship, often to those whose lack of resources render them least able to cope or recover. They add to a number of factors undermining centuries-old ways of life and threatening social and political stability in the Sahel.

Another assumption is that the objective of control operations is to bring a plague to an end. Yet it is generally agreed that climatic conditions have the most significant effects on plagues. PRIFAS has suggested that the end of the 1988 plague was brought about in precisely this way: 80% of the mortality at the end of 1988 being caused by the dry and cool conditions and the wind systems that carried swarms into the ocean. Only 20% of the deaths was due to control operations [4]. It is important, therefore, that the proportion of pests that will be killed by the control operations is carefully targeted—in places and at times to specifically prevent them from damaging crops. *Climate has the most significant effect on plagues*

Thus ideally those in charge of control operations should have the capacity to treat pest populations specifically to protect crops in the areas most at risk—and not to treat pests which pose no danger to production because they are, for example, likely to die or remain outside vulnerable areas. The earlier description of the difficulties of managing control programmes gives an idea of the standards of information and flexibility that such decision-making would require.

Finally, some argue that there is no need for any control measures, on the basis that locust plagues are naturally occuring phenomena which both develop and collapse through self-regulatory processes. However, the argument that we should leave well alone ignores the essential question of equity, fails to acknowledge the real if localised effects of plagues, and does not take account of the considerable potential for improved control and prevention measures. For, despite the difficulties described in this dossier, progress can be made. It might appear to be of lower priority than some of the other sources of poverty in the Sahel but compared with, say, the issues of international debt or global terms of trade, pest management is a concrete area of work that can be grappled with and results produced.

Information

The first area of prevention and control operations— surveillance and early warning—is one where there is considerable scope for improvement. Much of this potential lies in the use of remote sensing by satellite. A major need is to find ways of efficiently and rapidly getting the remotely sensed information to the users in the field. There is also room for improving the quality of the imagery and the expertise of the users who must interpret it.

George Popov

Using a greenness map to check satellite data about breeding sites against the situation in the field, Mali.

Ground survey work will always be necessary, both to collect information that cannot be gathered by remote methods and also for verification and calibration of satellite data. Some of the observations required will be new to many scouts. For example, hand-held position indicators now exist that can provide a precise location for each observation which can then be related directly to satellite maps. Thus the equipping, training and motivation of scouts is vital.

There is some work in progress in this area—for example, the preparation of a Desert Locust habitat atlas—but there is room for complementary studies and for computerisation and coordination of this work. FAO, UNDP and other donors are funding activities along these lines. An example from work on another regional pest, the tsetse fly, indicates the potential. Researchers in Oxford, England, have managed to establish links between information in greenness maps and the reproductive potential of the tsetse fly. This enables them to produce maps of its likely breeding grounds and indicate areas where there is greatest danger of the flies spreading disease [5].

Remote sensing systems were not designed to obtain information on insect activity. But they might have greater possibilities of doing so than have been appreciated by the meteorologists and geographers who are their primary users.

Similarly, recalibration might make the systems more usefully attuned to work in the Sahel. For example, the greenness maps might be of much greater use if the patterns of radiation from Sahelian crops at different stages were known. Even relatively crude distinctions between cropland, rangeland and wasteland could be helpful.

The great need is for better quality survey information

Combinations of complementary remote sensing systems— covering for example, wind movement, ground moisture, terrain and rainfall—are likely to yield more useful results than dependence on a few. Satellites are collecting information anyway; some modifications to the nature of collection and some imagination in interpretation seems to offer great possibilities for improved and cheaper control.

Access to satellite images and training in their interpretation are legitimate areas for donor support, and USAID has funded such activities. The immediate aim must be to build up good descriptions of the factors affecting grasshoppers and locusts so that, if they could then be picked up by satellite, predictions of their activity would improve and so would control measures. This is important because the resources to carry out effective ground surveys are limited; the areas to be surveyed on the ground should be reduced to those most likely to be the source of gregarised locusts. Good collection of ecological information is also likely to be of use for more than pest management, for example for agricultural monitoring and assessments of food production and security. And when there is conflict or insecurity in large parts of the Sahel, reliance on satellite imagery is all the greater.

Events in late 1992 and early 1993 in East Africa suggested strongly that a Desert Locust plague could once more be brewing, starting in the Red Sea hills region of Sudan, Eritrea and Saudi Arabia. The FAO *Desert Locust Bulletin* of January 1993 made it clear that the continuing great need is for better quality of survey information. It contained numerous "strong recommendations" to provide better information by intensifying surveying and monitoring, and warned of an upsurge which had all the characteristics of those which lead to plagues [6].

Pest biology
Current understanding of the biology of grasshoppers and locusts contains certain weaknesses, and special consideration should be given to proposals for work in these areas. Sahelian

institutions are often poorly equipped to support such research. Where there seems to be no appropriate institution, the possibility of funding individuals should be considered and any proposals from institutions in industrialised countries should be examined for possible involvement of Sahelians.

The FAO should be encouraged to take a more active role in the exchange of information. The review of current research could be broadened. Rather than the rather passive "listings" approach, positive recommendations could be made about gaps in research. An even more active approach would be to get funding for the research and then advertise for proposals to carry out the work. The Scientific Advisory Committee of the UNDP/FAO Consultative Group on Locust Research as well as other FAO committees and a number of donors are beginning to do this.

The key points of workshops and seminars could be summarised and made accessible to non-specialists. FAO, in its regular bulletin "Updates" on the Desert Locust situation, could be explicit about where information is missing and offer more in the way of interpretation, and more actively work to improve the quality and regularity of data coming in at national level. In 1992, certain gaps in the information in the bulletins indicated that no survey work was being reported to Rome, and may not even have been carried out.

There is a case for reviving a journal of applied work in grasshopper and locust control. Its coverage could include pest biology, Sahelian ecology, pesticide effectiveness, methods of survey and prediction, loss assessment etc. Many would argue that a targeted abstracting service, capable of searching databases across the world and pinpointing relevant publications, would be even more useful.

Above all, the creation of a single comprehensive and authoritative starting point for all those concerned with grasshopper and locust control would be very beneficial. The cost of pulling together the relevant information is insignificant. While a number of information networks exist, FAO remains the best forum for the exchange of ideas between scientists, administrators and decision-makers. But some feel that it has to re-earn the right to be in this position of authority, and researchers, donors and governments have to be prepared to invest FAO with the information and confidence it needs to do so.

There is a need to raise awareness about the dangers of chemical poisoning, and to safely dispose of the large quantities of surplus pesticides in the Sahel.

Pesticides

The campaigns during 1985-90 saw the testing and use of a wide range of pesticides new to grasshopper and locust control in the Sahel. A number show promise and may be more effective than the standard fenitrothion. More trials are needed, not only on their effectiveness against pests but also against non-target organisms. In the past, such work stopped during periods of recession—obviously, large swarms cannot be targeted for tests during these times. However, laboratory and field station tests could continue, and since 1989 this has been the case to a greater extent.

Pesticide companies work to economic imperatives. They are unlikely to invest in more effective products if the eventual market is too small to repay the research and development costs. A more realistic approach would be to concentrate on

Agencies should involve farmers more in research

identifying the best products among those already available.

Similarly, work on better application methods is driven by the needs of the major users of pesticides: those in industrialised countries. The main returns for producing better equipment will come from them, rather than from cash crop producers in developing countries. The sudden flood of money available for emergency campaigns is probably not consistent enough for researchers to concentrate effectively on developing better methods specifically for locust control. However, the general principle of work in this field—to employ less pesticide more effectively—is the same whatever the pest involved, so any innovations should be monitored for potential use.

For example, micro-encapsulation—when the product is enclosed in tiny plastic spheres to improve distribution, attachment to target plants and the active life of the product—may prove valuable in a number of pest management situations. So might the use of poison baits. Described as a relatively safe and effective means of distributing pesticides—more discriminating than dusting or spraying—the use of baits raises various practical problems, not least in knowing exactly where and when they can be used. What is needed is a thorough evaluation of the potential of these ideas for grasshopper and locust control, and the possible modifications. Relatively modest amounts of money can be sufficient to refine a promising method.

Other Technologies

Perhaps the greatest potential for progress lies outside the area of synthetic pesticides. But the development of other methods and means to control pests is not so much in order to replace such pesticides but to create a more integrated range of methods which would lead to a reduced, more judicious use of the synthetics.

The areas which show potential are: microbial control agents, of which the fungi *Beauveria bassiana* and *Metarhizium* show particular promise; neem and other local plant extracts which can operate as anti-feedants; natural "signal" chemicals—produced by insects (pheromones) or plants (allomones)—which influence insects' behaviour; and insect growth regulators which, although synthetic, are considered safer than pesticides because they act by disrupting

insect development, and are more specific to the intended *An insurance*
target organisms. Changes in weeding, planting and harvesting *premium*
methods show promise, particularly for the control of *approach is*
grasshoppers, as does egg-pod surveying and destruction. All *needed*
these different methods need developing and require varying
degrees of research time and trials, and therefore funding.

In these and other areas of work, there is also a need to get
away from the hermetically sealed, elitist approach to research:
organisations need to pay more attention to the applicability
and impact of research, and national level agencies should
involve farmers more in defining research objectives and
conducting trials.

Crisis or Chronic Problem?

The major strategic decision concerning locusts and
grasshoppers is the definition of their status: are they to be
seen as a persistent problem or an intermittent disaster?

An FAO coordination meeting in April 1990 to plan the
grasshopper control campaign in the Sahel agreed that the
problems were chronic and should not be treated as
emergencies. While this acknowledged that an insurance
premium approach is needed and that short-term funding is not
the answer, the debate must be won not only among
representatives to FAO but also among the decision-makers of
the major donor agencies and of the affected countries.

The problem with disaster or emergency funding is that it is
turned off as suddenly as it is released, which is more
appropriate for natural disasters like earthquakes than it is for
"creeping disasters" of a biological nature such as pest
outbreaks, particularly since it is not conducive to finding
long-term solutions. "When the current crisis is subdued,
locust/grasshopper control will revert to an unfunded priority.
Poof, it will disappear until a crisis again arises!" was the
lament of one 1987 USAID project paper [7].

Since 1989, there has been more response to such fears and
criticisms. It is clear that donors are more aware that
significant results require sustained and appropriate levels of
funding and that they are attempting to provide this.

But funders have to be reassured that progress is being
made not only in the development and research projects they
support but also in complementary work. Those who make the
decisions over competing demands for funding look for

Donors are a powerful force for change assurance that projects will achieve their objectives. The current pattern—to approve projects usually lasting a few years—is one that could be challenged. The head of the International Centre for Insect Physiology and Ecology (ICIPE) in Nairobi, Professor Thomas Odhiambo, said in a speech in London in 1990 that donors should consider funding some research projects for a minimum of 10 years [8]. The state of current knowledge more than justifies such an approach.

Training

A more long-term approach should also be applied to training and institutional support. The importance of training is cited in many documents on the future of grasshopper and locust control, but it is not a panacea and it rarely produces rapid results.

A prerequisite of successful training is a thorough understanding of the position of the trainee. It is not clear that this exists or is even acknowledged as necessary. It means adopting a longer time-scale and more cautious preparation, in order to match different levels of requirement with the options available. It is vital to build in a preparatory phase, during which the trainees' level of background knowledge and motivation can be ascertained and they can gain a real understanding of the purpose of the training. The training itself should be closely linked to practice. Immediate feedback on a training course is useful but real evaluation of its effectiveness will take much longer.

Subsidies

The major donors are a powerful force for change in grasshopper and locust control. The Sahelian states cannot afford emergency operations and at present cannot afford adequate monitoring and preventive operations either. The national plant protection services were already chronically underfunded when they took over the responsibility for migrant pests from the regional organisations. Donors have to accept the responsibility that comes with power over the purse: they should assist current control measures in the short term and in the long term work towards the Sahelian states being able to carry out this work with less support.

Reinforcement of state services has not been a popular option for many donors in the past, but a case for doing so in plant protection can be made. A more effective service will help the move towards greater self-sufficiency. And the price of not helping is likely to be far more expensive emergency operations and greater insecurity, dependence and suffering. The challenge is to find ways of supporting the development of strong government services in societies where there is increasing democratisation and decentralisation.

"What information there is, does not justify pesticide subsidies"

Finding cost-effective ways of supporting national crop protection services is a complex task. One analysis of the situation in Mali highlights the difficulties [9]. The donor-funded national crop protection service, the SNPV (Service National de Protection des Végétaux), was created in 1987, during the large-scale spraying campaigns of 1985-88. Although the threat from the Desert Locust and the Senegalese Grasshopper had died down by 1988, the SNPV and hundreds of village brigades remained in place. What was to be the role of the SNPV without an emergency campaign budget, or that of the brigades trained to use free insecticides?

The crop protection service was "young", with experience limited to short-term emergency measures, so the Malian government and its donors adapted the emergency approach. But by continuing on a long-term basis a policy of centralising decision-making, appealing for pesticides and mobilising spray campaigns, other ways of operating were not fully explored. A similar process is thought to have occurred in Burkina Faso, Niger and Senegal.

Given the difficulties that most Sahelian governments would have in financing the recurrent costs of crop protection, donor funding is clearly necessary but the scale implied by adapting an emergency approach is, according to Alex Kremer, author of the report on Mali, "financially unsustainable, stunts recipient organisations and is probably economically wasteful....There are too many pesticide/pest/crop/price/weather permutations [to establish the exact economic returns of pesticide use in the Sahel but]...what information there is does not justify pesticide subsidies [10]."

A long-term strategy based on subsidised insecticides has more than financial implications. At least 80% of all agricultural pesticide use in the Sahel is subsidised. This biases decision-making towards pesticide use and thus limits the exploration of alternatives. Among other things, it also provides incentives for reports of pest attacks to be exaggerated and it reduces the role of the national service to a

NGOs can strengthen links between state services and farmers supplier of free pesticides. Kremer makes several recommendations, including using an economist to evaluate plant protection projects where possible, featuring more cost-benefit analysis in research into control in the field, and the establishment of a reserve fund for local insecticide purchases from which money could be released only by a donor's committee and only to areas where they are satisfied an "emergency" has been declared.

Non-Government Organisations

NGOs, operating as they do at the grassroots level, have a narrower range of roles to play than multilaterals and bilaterals but they are nonetheless important. The first is much the same as the larger donors': to provide support, on a smaller scale, but widely distributed. The NGO coordinating bodies and the national crop protection services should together identify possible areas of collaboration. Where such consultation is lacking, NGO representatives should approach the national services for information. The scale of assistance is always likely to be small but its timing and nature could be significant. The largest single NGO action was probably the purchase by LiveAid of a spray aircraft for the Malian service.

A more important role stems from the location of NGO projects, which are often in the remoter, more marginal areas where national services are notoriously weak. NGO staff can be valuable go-betweens, liaising with the communities they serve and the national services.

This can be a two-way process with, for example, NGOs passing on information and advice from the government extension service as well as relaying back information from the villages. This information might be about rainfall, the condition of vegetation and crops, or pest observations. One of the weakest links between the wide range of participants in locust control is that between farmers and the national services; NGOs have the very characteristics to help strengthen it. They can also help with the training of village brigades. Useful work has already been done along these lines, for example in the Dogon region of Mali. They could also be assisted to promote the development and extension of IPM. CARE (an international NGO), for example, has adopted an IPM policy worldwide, geared towards minimising pesticide use [11].

The staff of NGOs may feel that their first responsibility is to the communities with whom they work. This responsibility can be legitimately fulfilled by lobbying the national services and donors for better support in terms of protection from regional pests. It will bring farmers' voices into the debate over the best means of protection and bring farmers' knowledge and skills to the service of campaigns. The very fact that NGOs have only a limited scale of operation enables them to play this important role.

National Services

Those in Sahelian governments and plant protection services are probably those who operate under the greatest constraints. The greatest single limitation is simply the national budget. There is also great insecurity over funding, which can be as "on/off" as donors' emergency funding. A guaranteed budget is always preferable to on/off funding, even when total sums are lower. Without consistent funding, it is extremely difficult to equip, train or motivate staff. It is, however, possible to promote effective dialogue about more rational ways of sharing these costs. Many donor representatives are not specialists in pest management and would appreciate help from national staff in increasing their understanding of the complexities of the

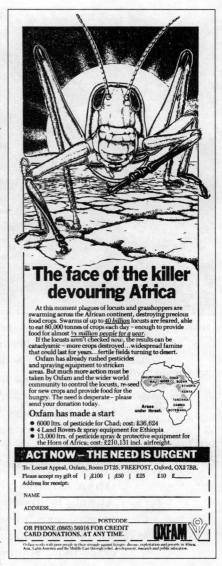

The face of the killer devouring Africa

At this moment plagues of locusts and grasshoppers are swarming across the African continent, destroying precious food crops. Swarms of up to 40 *billion* locusts are feared, able to eat 80,000 tonnes of crops each day – enough to provide food for almost ⅓ *million people for a year*.

If the locusts aren't checked *now*, the results can be cataclysmic – more crops destroyed...widespread famine that could last for years...fertile fields turning to desert.

Oxfam has already rushed pesticides and spraying equipment to stricken areas. But much more action must be taken by Oxfam and the wider world community to control the locusts, re-seed for new crops and provide food for the hungry. The need is desperate – please send your donation today.

Oxfam has made a start

- 6000 ltrs. of pesticide for Chad; cost: £36,624
- 4 Land Rovers & spray equipment for Ethiopia
- 13,000 ltrs. of pesticide spray & protective equipment for the Horn of Africa; cost: £210,131 incl. airfreight.

ACT NOW – THE NEED IS URGENT

To: Locust Appeal, Oxfam, Room DT25, FREEPOST, Oxford, OX2 7BR.
Please accept my gift of | £100 | £50 | £25 | £10 £____
Address for receipt:

NAME _____

ADDRESS_____

POSTCODE_____
OR PHONE (0865) 56916 FOR CREDIT CARD DONATIONS, AT ANY TIME.

OXFAM

Oxfam works with poor people in their struggle against hunger, disease, exploitation and poverty in Africa, Asia, Latin America and the Middle East through relief, development, research and public education.

task. Both donor organisations and national services need to find ways to improve and make the most of institutional memory—through developing policy guidelines, publications, training and re-training, and encouraging experienced staff.

NGOs have a role to play beyond emergency relief.

There has at times been considerable tension between donors and national services. The situation is improving. Donors have, in recent years, become more sensitive to the longer-term implications of aid and there is less of an air of patronage about funding negotiations.

Millet store, Niger. If the security of farming in the Sahel is to improve, well-funded but unsustained emergency responses need to give way to more consistent support for crop protection.

National services can foster this improved relationship by themselves bringing greater openness and clarity to discussions. It is legitimate to negotiate with donors for the most appropriate forms of aid, such as equipment, products or training that conform to local norms and practice. Equally, it is fair to tell donors' coordination meetings why a local service would be better served by a package of aid comprising, say, equipment from France, pesticides from the United States, training from Canada, or some similar combination.

Open minds

Although this chapter contains suggestions addressed to organisations, these are really appeals to individuals. Research will not become more appropriate until individual researchers make more appropriate proposals. These will not be funded until individuals in the appropriate institutions decide to support them. Funding will not consistently be put on a more reliable, longer-term base until individual members in the field and at the headquarters of donor organisations produce convincing proposals to do so. The same responsibilities lie with individuals in NGOs and national services.

Some of the complexities of grasshopper and locust control are specifically related to the insects' behaviour and their environment, but there are also lessons to be drawn from past experience which relate to development aid more generally. There has been an emphasis on short-term interventions, rather than on the strengthening of indigenous capabilities, both individual and institutional. There has been a tendency to tackle pest management in isolation from broader social, political and economic issues. The rural communities who are in the front line of defence against pest attack have not been sufficiently consulted or involved in the development of strategy or method. There has been over-dependence on environmentally risky practices, and insufficient attention paid to the development of alternative methods and products, which take greater account of local conditions. In short, there is a need for a more sustainable approach. All too often in the past, as the US Office of Technology Assessment has put it, "development goals [were] sacrificed in favour of emergency management [12]."

"Development goals were sacrificed in favour of emergency management"

Writing in October 1992, Professor Thomas Odhiambo warned of the juxtaposition of periodic locust plague to similarly recurrent drought. "The current drought in Southern

USAID *Crop Protection* clip art book

An illustration from a training manual designed to help extension workers strengthen local capacity to monitor pests and protect crops.

and Eastern Africa is already at least 18 months old. It is likely to be followed, when it does end, by the outbreak of different migratory pests....[there is now] a first-rate opportunity for scientists and technologists to find technologically efficient, environmentally sustainable and durable long-range methods to resolve these age-old migratory pest issues, so closely associated with vulnerable communities and fragile ecosystems [13]."

But action must be taken and supported at all levels; not just by scientists and technicians but also by farmers, trainers, extension agents, donors, manufacturers and policymakers. Genuine collaboration between these different groups, with their different priorities, has not been a strong feature of past strategies. This dossier does not suggest that there are any quick answers but rather that the situation demands the willingness to try new approaches. Open minds will be as important as open budgets; the greatest failure would be for Chapman's sad reflection to ring true in the 1990s.

Summary

The threat
- Locusts: Intermittent plague, normally only developing after a period of extended drought. Large-scale crop damage results, but impact not uniform. Gregarisation is a key factor in the build-up of plagues. Because the Desert Locust breeds in remote areas, the initial monitoring phase requires specialised technology and trained teams. During recessions, locusts present little threat to crops
- Grasshoppers: Annual crippling attacks on crops. Many different species are involved. Although damage is less dramatic than that caused by locusts, over the last 30 years the crops lost to grasshoppers are cumulatively more significant. Control activities vary with the seasons and are fairly time-sensitive, and farmers can play a critical role

The strategy
- Locusts: Ideally, to focus resources on prevention of build-up rather than crop protection—surveying, monitoring and controlling breeding patterns to keep populations below dangerous levels. Once plague proportions are reached, to target resources on crop protection in vulnerable areas rather than attempting to bring the plague to an end or even substantially reduce it
- Grasshoppers: Prevention is not so applicable, and large-scale spraying has little long-term effect. Better to concentrate control efforts on crop protection, but with improved monitoring and forecasting of grasshopper infestations

The circumstances
- The dramatic nature of plagues has encouraged massive emergency campaigns, followed by minimal activity during periods of quiescence
- Fluctuations in funding, as result of the emergency approach, have hindered attempts to make consistent improvements in crop protection or pest management
- Over-reliance on, and misuse and over-supply of chemical pesticides has carried human and environmental risks

- The largely subsistence nature of Sahelian farming and the unpredictability of the environment mean obtaining accurate data on crop production and loss is difficult
- National statistics are anyway misleading; losses are usually unevenly distributed
- There is no proven direct link between locust attack and famine
- Locust and grasshopper attack is just one of several factors undermining vulnerable rural communities in the Sahel
- Traditional methods of control exist but are insufficient by themselves when numbers rise to plague levels

- Pesticide spraying campaigns may be responsible for only about 20% of insect deaths when a plague collapses: weather conditions play the most important role
- Because the weather is such a key factor in the build-up and collapse of plagues, pest management is characterised by unpredictability
- The information gathering and exchange so vital to pest management is hampered in the Sahel by poor communication and transport systems, the huge distances involved and the insecurity in some key areas

What can be done?

Most experts agree that:

- There should be greater emphasis on reliable, **consistent funding** and the search for **long-term** solutions
- Support will be necessary for national crop protection services, but there is a need to reduce dependence on subsidised pesticides and on the crisis or emergency approach
- The **research** base needs to be built up: on the pests, their natural enemies and on Sahelian ecosystems
- More research is needed on **environmental effects** and on the **cost-effectiveness of pesticides**
- The monitoring and adaptation of related research, both practical and theoretical, could be improved
- FAO, with other donors, could be more pro-active over the **exchange of information** and stimulation of research

- **Communication** between donors could be improved, to minimise contradiction or duplication of effort
- The possibilities of greater **regional coordination** could be explored
- There is scope to explore and expand the potential and actual **role of NGOs** in prevention and control activities
- The farmers' strategy of **risk reduction** rather than risk avoidance needs greater recognition
- **Village brigades** can play a major part in campaigns, but only if resources are put into their training and supervision, and their health and safety properly protected
- The role of farmer brigades can be expanded beyond pesticide application
- More attention and support could be given to **training**, both practical and managerial

- Improved access to **satellite technology** and training in its interpretation and application would benefit control operations
- Ways need to be found to get remote sensing information more rapidly to staff in the field
- There is a need to improve the **reliability** and quality of **information** coming in from the field

- A **combination** of control methods is most likely to be fruitful, rather than over-reliance on one
- A reduced reliance on chemical pesticides looks possible, if sufficient support is given to the development of **alternatives**, such as bio-pesticides
- **Integrated Pest Management** techniques are currently most applicable for grasshopper control and need more research and development
- The **safe disposal** of large quantites of obsolete and surplus pesticides must be made a priority
- The ability to **target resources** at vulnerable crop areas should be developed, so minimising the use of pesticides and the associated environmental hazards

References

CHAPTER 1
1. Exodus, Chapter 10, verses 14-15.
2. Joel, Chapter 1, verse 4.
3. Quoted in *The Challenges of Drought: Ethiopia's decade of struggle in relief and rehabilitation*, Relief and Rehabilitation Commission, Addis Ababa, 1985, p280.
4. Waloff, Z, *The Upsurges and Recessions of the Desert Locust Plague: an historical survey*, Anti-Locust Memoir No 8, 1966.
5. Krebs, C J, *Ecology: the experimental analysis of distribution and abundance*, Harper & Row, New York, 1972, p293.
6. Chapman, R F, *A Biology of Locusts*, Studies in Biology: No 71, Edward Arnold, London, 1976, p63.
7. *A Plague of Locusts—Special Report*, US Congress, Office of Technology Assessment, OTA-F-450, Government Printing Office, Washington DC, July 19 1990, p4.

CHAPTER 2
1. See Abdel Rahim, Nafissa and others, *Greenwar: environment and conflict in the Sahel*, Panos Publications, London, 1991.
2. All these indented quotes from Sahelian farmers and pastoralists are taken from the Sahel Oral History Project, conducted by SOS Sahel, 1 Tolpuddle Street, London N1 OXT, and summarised in Cross, N and Baker, R (eds), *At the Desert's Edge: oral histories from the Sahel*, Panos Publications, London, 1991.
3. Webb, M, "Technical report on a visit to the Mali millet pest control project: June-November 1990", Natural Resources Institute, Chatham, UK.
4. *Tin Aica Nomad Village*, American Friends Service Council, Philadelphia, 1982.
5. For more discussion of the survival strategies of Sahelian people and the general tendency to more mixed agro-pastoral ways of life, see Bonfils, M, *Halte à la Desertification au Sahel*, Karthala/CTA, May 1987; Toulmin, C, *Cattle, Women and Wells: managing household survival in the Sahel*, Oxford University Press, 1992; Galley, J, *Strategies Pastoralistes et Agronomistes des Sahelians durant la Secheresse 1969-74*, CEGT, Paris, 1977; Oxby, C, "African livestock-keepers in recurrent crisis: policy issues arising from the NGO response", International Insititute for Environment and Development, London, September 1989; Cross, N, *The Sahel: the people's right to development*, Minority Rights Group, London, 1990; and Cross, N and Barker, R (eds), *At the Desert's Edge: oral histories from the Sahel*, op.cit.
6. Jago, N, "Report on crop loss due to major grasshopper attack in rainfed

areas of N.W. Mali, June-November 1989", 1990, unpublished report; see also "Mali millet pest control project: Agricultural economics report", by Lock, C, Mahmoud, M and Sidibe, A (1987), Lock, C, and Mahmoud, M (1988), and Lock, C (1989), internal documents, Natural Resources Institute, Chatham, UK.

7. For some discussion of the pros and cons of farmer surveys, see Lock, C, "Mali millet pest control project: Agricultural economics report", internal document, Natural Resources Institute, Chatham, UK, 1989.

8. Brader, L, "Locust and grasshopper control", *Haramata*, No 8, June 1990, International Institute for Environment and Development, London, pp20-21.

9. See Krebs, C J, *Ecology: the experimental analysis of distribution and abundance*, Harper & Row, New York, 1972, p289. Chapter 15 concerns locust populations.

10. Uvarov, B P, *Grasshoppers and Locusts: a handbook of general acridology*, Centre for Overseas Pest Research, London, 1977, p613.

11. Cross, N and Barker, R (eds), *At the Desert's Edge: oral histories from the Sahel*, op. cit., pp1 and 14.

12. See Abdel Rahim, Nafissa and others, *Greenwar: environment and conflict in the Sahel*, op. cit., 1991.

13. Information from Mohamed Hisham, Sudan, 1990.

14. See *Review of Environmental Concerns in A.I.D. Programs for Locust and Grasshopper Control in Africa*, USAID, Office of Technical Resources, publication No 91-7, Washington DC, September 1991.

CHAPTER 3

1. Nyiira, Zerubabel M, Regional FAMESA Project Coordinator, ICIPE, Nairobi, quoted in *A Plague of Locusts—A Special Report*, US Congress, Office of Technology Assessment, OTA-F-450, US Government Printing Office, Washington DC, July 1990, p23.

2. Uvarov, B P, "A revision of the genus *Locusta* with a new theory as to the periodicity and migrations of locusts", *Bulletin Entomol Res 12*, 1921, pp135-63.

3. Excellent detailed descriptions of the important species of locusts and grasshoppers of the Sahel can be found in a number of publications. See, for example, Steedman, A (ed), *Locust Handbook* (3rd edition), Natural Resources Institute, Chatham, 1988; Duranton, J-F, Launois, M, Launois-Luong, M H, Lecoq, M and Rachardi, T, *Guide Antiacridien du Sahel*, CIRAD, Paris, 1987; Lecoq, M, *Les Criquets du Sahel*, Acridologie Operationelle, No 1, CIRAD/PRIFAS, Montpellier, 1988; Popov, G B, *Nymphs of the Sahelian Grasshoppers: an illustrated guide*, Natural Resources Institute, Chatham, UK, 1989; and Mestre, J, *Les Acridiens des Formations Herbeuses d'Afrique de l'Ouest*, Ministère de la Coopération and CIRAD/PRIFAS, Paris, 1988.

4. *A Plague of Locusts—A Special Report*, op. cit., p26.

CHAPTER 4

1. See Lecoq, M, "Les biomodèles en acridologie et leurs applications operationnelle", *Raport de la reunion sur la recherche antiacridienne*, FAO, Rome, 18-20 October, 1988, pp79-99; and Coste, C and others, "Exploitation du biomodèle OSE4 specifique à *Oedaleus senegalensis* (Krauss, 1877)", CIRAD/PRIFAS, Montpellier, 1992.

CHAPTER 6

1. There are a number of excellent texts which look in detail at the technical methods of pest control used in grasshopper and locust campaigns. See, for example, Steedman, A (ed), *Locust Handbook* (3rd edition), Natural Resources Institute, Chatham, 1988; Duranton, J-F, Launois, M, Launois-Luong, M H, Lecoq, M and Rachardi, T, *Guide Antiacridien du Sahel*, CIRAD, Paris, 1987; Launois, M, *Manuel Pratique d'Identification des Principaux Acridiens du Sahel*, Ministère de la Coopération and GERDAT, Paris, 1978; and *Locust/Grasshopper Management Operations Handbook*, USAID, Washington DC, January 1989.
2. See Debach, P, "Some recipes for fostering pests", *Biological Control by Natural Enemies*, Cambridge University Press, UK, 1974, p323.
3. Brader, L, "Locust and grasshopper control", *Haramata*, No 8, June 1990, International Institute for Environment and Development, London, pp20-21.
4. See Ricklefs, R E, *Ecology*, Nelson, London, 1973, p861.
5. Information from a Desert Locust Control Committee meeting, FAO, Rome, September 1992.
6. *The Desert Locust Research and Development Register*, FAO, Rome.
7. Chapman, R F, *A Biology of Locusts*, Studies in Biology: No 71, Edward Arnold, London, 1976, p63.
8. There is a little experimental evidence from the field to support this. See Everts, J, "Environmental effects of locust control", *PAN Europe 3*, No 10, 1988, pp19-21.
9. Private conversation. For some comments at the time of the decision, see MacKenzie, D, "Locusts thrive as pesticide ban stays", *New Scientist*, London, 31 March, 1988, p17, and "Call to unleash dieldrin on locust plague", *New Scientist*, London, 15 September, 1988, pp26-27.
10. See Knausenberger, W I, Andreasen, J and Belayneh, Y T, "West African regional AID pesticide disposal conference: disposal of pesticide containers and obselete pesticides", report of conference in Niamey, Niger, January 1990, USAID, Washington DC.
11. Bull, D, *A Growing Problem: pesticides and the Third World*, Oxfam, Oxford, 1982, p192.
12. "Synopsis of 1991 research on development of the fungus *Beauveria bassiana* for grasshopper control in Africa", USAID, Washington DC, January 1992. The programme is carried out by Montana State University in collaboration with Cape Verde and Malian scientists.
13. See Lomer, C J and Prior, C, "Biological control of locusts and grasshoppers: proceedings of a workshop held at IITA, Cotonou, Benin, 29 April-1 May 1991", CAB International, Wallingford, UK.
14. Ibid.
15. "Locust/Grasshopper strategy paper," Africa Bureau, USAID, Washington DC, February 1987.
16, *Locust/Grasshopper Management Operations Guidebook*, op. cit.
17. "Cube-Expert", CIRAD/PRIFAS, Montpellier, 1988—a cube designed by TM Luong with different information on each face.

CHAPTER 7

1. *Locust/Grasshopper Management Operations Guidebook*, USAID, Washington DC, January 1989.

2. Teng, P S, "Plant protection systems in West and Central Africa—a situation analysis," report prepared for FAO Plant Protection Service, Rome, 1985.
3. Popov, G B, "A note on Oxfam's contribution towards fighting the Desert Locust plague in Mali during the 1988 campaign", communication with Oxfam representative in Mali, December 1988.
4. Sources for tables are—Column 1: Roffey, J, "1986 Funding chart for grasshopper and locust campaigns in Africa", Emergency Centre for Locust Operations, Rome, December 1986; Column 2: "Report of the meeting on the evaluation of the 1987 Grasshopper Campaign in the Sahel", Annex VI, Emergency Centre for Locust Operations, Rome, December 1987; Columns 3 and 4: FAO, "Assistance provided to countries and regional organizations", Report of the Thirtieth Session of the FAO Desert Locust Control Commitee, AGP:DLCC/89/4, Rome, June 12-16, 1989.

CHAPTER 8

1. Chapman, R F, *A Biology of Locusts*, Studies in Biology: No 71, Edward Arnold, London, 1976, p65.
2. See, for example, Showler, A T and Potter, C S, "Synopsis of the 1986-89 Desert Locust plague and the concept of strategic control", *American Entomologist*, Vol 37, No 2, Summer 1991, pp106-110.
3. *A Plague of Locusts—Special Report*, US Congress, Office of Technology Assessment, OTA-F-450, Government Printing Office, Washington DC, July 1990, p9.
4. *PRIFAS SAS newsletter 13*, CIRAD, Montpellier, 1989.
5. Rogers, D J, and Randolph, S E, "Mortality rates and population density of tsetse flies correlated with satellite imagery", *Nature*, Vol 351, 1991, pp739-741.
6. *Desert Locust Bulletin*, FAO, No 173, January 1993.
7. The Africa Emergency Locust/Grasshopper Assistance project, USAID, Washington DC, March 17, 1987.
8. Opening address, annual general meeting of SOS Sahel UK, London, 1990.
9. Kremer, A, "Pests and donors in Mali, 1985-90", *Disasters*, Vol 16, No 3, 1992.
10. Ibid., p214.
11. Matteson, P, "CARE's IPM policies for developing countries", *IPM Practitioner*, Vol 14 (5/6), May-June 1992, pp15-16.
12. *A Plague of Locusts—Special Report*, op. cit., p10.
13. Odhiambo, T, "The challenge of locusts in drought-prone environments", *Stop Disasters*, newsletter of International Decade for Natural Disaster Reduction, Geneva, No 9, September/October 1992.